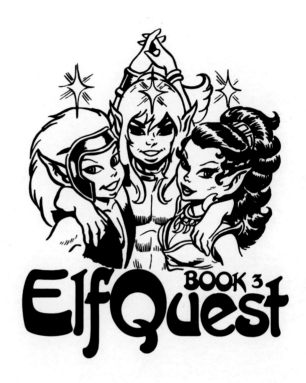

ElfQuest Book 3 contains the story found in issues eleven through fifteen of the black and white *ElfQuest* magazine published by WaRP Graphics.

Other titles in this series:
ElfQuest Book 1
ElfQuest Book 2
ElfQuest Book 3 is one of many graphic novels published by The Donning Company/ Publishers. For a complete listing of our titles, please write to the address below. Please include $1.00 for postage and handling. **ElfQuest Book 1** ($9.95) and **ElfQuest Book 2** ($10.95) can be ordered directly from the publisher at the retail price plus $1.00 per book shipping and handling.

The Donning Company/Publishers
5659 Virginia Beach Boulevard
Norfolk, Virginia 23502

First Printing October 1983

Library of Congress Cataloging in Publication Data:

Pini, Wendy
    Elfquest
    Consists mainly of material originally published in ElfQuest.
    Summary: Volume 3 of the full color illustrated fantasy adventure of the Wolfriders, a band of elves searching for others of their kind in a savage Earthlike world.
        1. Fantasy. 2. Fairies - Fiction
        I. Pini, Richard   II. Title.
PS3566.I524E4   813'.54   81-5401
ISBN 0-89865-329-0 (pbk. : v. 3)
ISBN 0-89865-328-2 (lim. ed. : v. 3)

Printed in the United States of America

Commentaries on the Quest

In the afterword to **ElfQuest Book 2,** Wendy and Richard Pini wrote: *Somewhere along the way we must have turned into elves.* Why not, I thought? The story of how they originally met is certainly as whimsical as any elf's adventure.

Wendy (in California) had written a letter to the editor of Marvel's *Silver Surfer.* Richard (at college in Massachusetts) read it and, taken by its positive tone, decided to write back. Thus began a four-year correspondence during which they actually got together about once a year. Their phone bills gradually became outrageous. "It was finally cheaper to get married," is Richard's wry summing up.

Thus began not only their own marriage, but the marriage of their distinctive talents out of which **ElfQuest** was born.

"It's at least eighty percent autobiographical," Wendy says. "Some comedian once answered the question of where he got his material from with the observation that the most personal things are the most universal. **ElfQuest,** as one of our fans pointed out, is really a self-quest. It is a very personal story; a journey that we, too, have undertaken. It reflects not only the things that have happened to us but the changes in our relationship—our personal growth through the seven years of sticking to this project and not giving up even when that was awfully tempting.

"In **ElfQuest** we have no archetypes, no Darth Vader representing evil or Luke Skywalker representing good. No single-faceted characters as such because what we've wanted to give them is the capacity to grow. We always say: **ElfQuest** isn't a battle of good versus evil, it's a battle of knowledge versus ignorance. Some of our fans complain that our characters have lost their innocence. I have to say to them: Of course, how do you grow otherwise?"

Cutter's encounter with the squirrel (**ElfQuest Book 2**) was taken almost directly from real life. The protagonist, however, was Richard—still in college at the time. While taking a walk near the college chapel which had a moat around it, he happened to see a squirrel in the moat. The squirrel, struggling and twisting about, was apparently drowning although there was hardly any water in the moat. Richard, always the humanitarian, got a stick and held it out to the squirrel. The ungrateful creature scampered up the stick and promptly began gnawing on Richard's thumb.

The firefly love scene (**ElfQuest Book 2**) was another experience lifted almost directly from life and incorporated into the book. It happened one evening in Bridgewater, Massachusetts. Richard and Wendy, then living in an apartment complex with woods and a river out in back, went walking one night along the trail that ran by the river. There they came upon a baby bird which had fallen out of its nest. They took it home to examine it for injuries and, finding none, brought it back to where they'd found it, laying it down near some low-hanging willow branches.

The evening was well along by this time. For no clear reason, perhaps only chance, they parted the willow branches and disclosed an open field in which all the trees growing by the little winding river were filled with fireflies.

"It was as if every star in the sky had fallen into this field," Wendy recalls. "It was a totally magic moment. We started walking through this field of star-filled trees and not one thing flew at us or bit us. When we got back to the apartment we just sat there staring at each other. We tried to recreate this experience the following night. We figured the fireflies would be out again. It was probably the mating season for them.

"They were there all right. But we couldn't walk more than a few feet before we turned back. There are some moments you can't recreate. To preserve it somehow I decided to put it into **ElfQuest.**"

In this manner many of the Pini's experiences have been transformed into part and parcel of **ElfQuest.** In this process of transformation, they find, the initial event takes on heightened meaning for them. Thus they grow through their experiences.

As one would expect in a story based so heavily on its authors' inner lives, their respective personalities become visible in those of their creations; Cutter getting his impulsiveness, his buoyant energy from Wendy, and Skywise his pragmatism and reflective nature from Richard. Like Wendy, Cutter would prefer to play, to dream, to go swinging high off the ground through the trees rather than be weighted by the responsibilities of his "quest." And, like Richard, Skywise's scientific mind, his practical earthy wisdom, play an indispensable part in helping Cutter keep the balance between responsibilities and dreams.

The dream that did eventually blossom as **ElfQuest** had been germinating for many years. Its beginning can already be seen in the drawings Wendy did as a child. Elves, fairies, fantasy creatures, had always intrigued her. As her artistic skill developed, so did the freshness and charm of her drawings as well as her unique knack for capturing emotion in facial expressions.

It was in 1977, however, when Wendy said to Richard, "I have an idea I'd like to bounce off you," that it first began to take definite shape.

"Naturally it was a great deal less formed than it is now," Richard explains. "Still, the ideas for the entire story were in that initial conversation. The details have grown. The firmness has grown. Somewhere along the way we knew how many issues it would take and what events were going to take place in each issue. In rough form, though, it was all planned from the beginning. We had to have a goal to reach. We had to know where we were going to go."

Richard and Wendy express once having had the fanciful idea which, I think, must pass through all our minds at one point or another: If I am a success then I won't have to work so hard anymore. It's a naive idea, they have found, completely innocent of the consequences and responsibilities of success.

"With each new issue I feel that I have to top the last," Wendy says.

Richard always has to remind her: "We're doing this because we want to do it. Don't be so hard on yourself. We're supposed to be having fun."

"It is true," Wendy reflects. "There are times that I've been at the drawing board till four in the morning and I have been able to say: Well, I've worked myself to pieces but it looks good. It feels good. I am having fun."

Having followed the adventures of Wendy and Richard's irrepressible elves, I can enthusiastically say that anyone about to join them on their "quest" will be having fun, too.

Boris Vallejo
New York, 1983

I first saw **ElfQuest** back in 1978 when volume one appeared. Saw, but ignored, because I read books, not comics, and I'd been reading about both elves and quests for a long time. I didn't think a comic book was going to have anything new to say on either subject. I kept on ignoring the project right into 1982, though the accumulation of issues, moving in a cherished, guarded stack from bedrooms to living room; read and re-read by everyone else in the house, was getting hard to ignore by that time.

It might have even been a dark and stormy night—it was certainly a night when no one else was around to witness my capitulation. I read the first dozen or so volumes in one sitting, re-read them as well. Wendy's artwork probably caught me first. The **ElfQuest** art does not simply illustrate; it is all of the story not contained in the necessarily limited dialogue. For once, I wasn't looking at a comic book where the words and pictures were competing for my attention and the bookworm in me didn't feel cheated.

In an important way, though, I was fortunate to have a substantial part of the story in my lap when I started. **ElfQuest** is, first and foremost, a single story. Everything that will be revealed by the final page is foreshadowed in the beginning. (And no—I don't *know* the ending; Richard simply wouldn't say anything when I asked if he and Wendy had, indeed, followed that ancient rule of story-

telling.) And yet, there are unfoldings and convolutions in each issue which, to date at least, have complicated the quest as much as they have resolved it. The events have to be absorbed for themselves then appreciated in the larger context of the entire quest. I guess that's why I re-read the entire story now each time a new volume occurs. The true rhythm of **ElfQuest** is not the pulse-racing sameness of other so-called quests where disaster emerges from nowhere whenever resolution is in sight—despite the number of times that the Wolfriders have seemed to encounter the unsolvable. Wendy and Richard have always known the story they intended to tell and exactly how to tell it.

Because **ElfQuest** has always been one story, and after six years of telling a quest itself for those who have followed it from the beginning, it has developed both the completeness and mystery of our most enduring epics. The gradual, yet complex, single-minded evolution of the story is the stuff from which myths have always been made. There is a completeness to the words and pictures, not to mention that four-month gap between issues, that allows the reader to enter the story and move beyond its marked boundaries. In an age where "instant"-everything is the norm, WaRP Graphics has forced us backward to a time when the storyteller, who was the only one who knew the whole story-cycle, told the tale at its most tantalizing pace and left the audience to its own imagination the rest of the time.

That part of the quest which is here in **ElfQuest Book 3** took over a year to be revealed by WaRP. It took longer to read than it took the elves to live. The storytellers, Wendy and Richard, made certain that every word was heard, every symbol examined, and every emotion felt in the heart of their readers. It will be different for those holding this book who do not already know the lessons of Blue Mountain. The whole drama is in your hands: Winnowill, Lord Voll, Wendy's most evocative art to date, and more to be devoured in one sitting, as I did that dark and stormy night. Then you can join the rest of us waiting...waiting a full one-hundred and twenty days from unfolding to unfolding...knowing the quest will end, perhaps imagining how—but not really *knowing*—and so, waiting for the privilege of sharing the conclusion of **ElfQuest** with the Wolfriders.

—Lynn Abbey
Ann Arbor, 1983

ElfQuest BOOK 3

by Wendy and Richard Pini

Art by Wendy Pini
Colors by Wendy Pini
with Joe Barruso, M. Lucie Chin
and Jane Fancher

With commentary by:
Boris Vallejo and Lynn Abbey
Afterwords by Wendy and Richard Pini
Edited by Kay Reynolds • Starblaze Graphics
Donning • Norfolk/Virginia Beach • 1983

≶SIGH≶ DISAPPOINTING... PREDICTABLY UNIMAGINATIVE.

I FIND IT HARD TO BELIEVE THAT THESE SMALL, *BRUTISH* CREATURES ARE IN ANY WAY RELATED TO US.

BUT THEY ARE, *TYLDAK.* ISN'T IT AMUSING?

HOW LIKE FRANTIC *BEASTS* THEY SEEM!

SEE THIS SILENT ONE'S SHARP, TEARING TEETH?

SEE HOW HE *SNARLS* WITH RAGE?

BOTH HE AND HIS MATE WOULD REND US TO PIECES...IF THEY COULD!

LET HIM GO!!

LET HIM GO OR-- I'LL KILL YOU!!

AN INTERESTING CHALLENGE..!

DO YOU THINK YOU CAN TAKE MY LIFE, LITTLE ONE--

--BEFORE I TAKE HIS..?

STOP!! STOP TORTURING HIM!

PLEASE!

OH, PLEASE STOP!!

HE DESERVES TO SUFFER FOR HIS CRIME!

:SOB:

STRONGBOW... MY LIFEMATE... FORGIVE ME!

AT THE MOUNTAIN'S BASE A FAR MORE PEACEFUL SCENE TAKES PLACE.

THE MOONS ARE FULL, AND EACH WEARS A RING OF MISTY LIGHT!

WILL THE STRANGE HONORED ONE SPEAK TO US TO-NIGHT, DO YOU THINK?

HE WILL NOT TAKE OUR OFFERINGS IF WE STAY AND WATCH FOR HIM...

PATIENCE! BY AND BY HE WILL LET US KNOW HIS WILL!

I HAVE GLIMPSED HIM IN THE SHADOWS; HE IS FIERCE TO BEHOLD, SURROUNDED BY GREAT BEASTS OF THE NIGHT..!

HE DOES NOT FLY UPON A *BOND-BIRD* LIKE HIS FELLOWS.

THAT *IS* STRANGE.

BUT WE MUST NOT QUESTION THE WAYS OF THE *BIRD SPIRITS.*

THEY HAVE SENT US A MESSENGER WHO WILL SPEAK TO US IN HIS OWN TIME--

--AND IN HIS OWN WAY!

COME! THERE IS MUCH LEFT TO BE DONE FOR THE *CEREMONY.*

SNIFF!

THREE NIGHTS IN A ROW AND THEY *STILL* HAVEN'T TRIED TO *POISON* US!

I COULD ALMOST BELIEVE THESE HUMANS MEAN US NO *ILL!*

HAH! THAT'LL BE THE DAY!

BUT FOOD IS FOOD, WHETHER WE HUNT IT OR *STEAL* IT, EH FRIENDS?

AYE, SMOKE-TREADER...

THEY'RE UP THERE ALL RIGHT...

CLEARBROOK, SCOUTER, AND THE OTHERS.

I'D GIVE MY *ONLY EYE* TO KNOW HOW THEY FARE!

BUT I DON'T *DARE* SEND!

THERE'S A POWERFUL *ENEMY* INSIDE THAT MOUNTAIN!

ONE WHO CAN *BLOCK* MY SENDING-- TURN IT *AGAINST* ME!

BUT DON'T WORRY, FRIEND! *SOMEHOW* I'LL FIND A WAY TO *FREE* THE WOLF-RIDERS!

EH? SOMETHING ON THE WIND..?

ONE-EYE WATCHES THE WOLVES CLOSELY.

WHUF!

THE LANGUAGE OF THEIR BODIES IS *ELOQUENT.* SOMEONE IS COMING...

...SOMEONE WHO IS YET FAR AWAY... BREE DEE DEE DREEJ DREEJ DEE DEE DIRI DIRI BREEDEEJ DEEE

BREE DEE DEEPLE DREEJ

ENOUGH! SCAVENGER BIRDS SING BETTER THAN *THAT!*

PETALWING SING VERY NICE!

HEY, BUG! OOO! THERE'S A *MOUSE* ASLEEP IN THAT HOLLOW LOG! GO WRAP IT UP!

IT WON'T WORK! ANYTHING FOR A MOMENT'S PEACE!

GRR!

BAP HIGHTHING FIBBEP! WAS NO STILLQUIET, FURSOFT GRAPLEBABY THERE! PETAL-WING VEXEP!

NO YOU DON'T, BUG! THIS TIME I'M *READY* FOR YOU!

SPLOOZT!

YEEPH!

:BLUBBER MOOFLE WHINE!:

CALMLY, TINY FRIEND! NOW IS NOT A GOOD TIME FOR SINGING!

LOOK AT *FIRECOAT* AND *WOODSHAVER*! THEY SENSE THE REST OF THE PACK SOMEWHERE IN THE DISTANCE!

THE WOLFPACK WILL BE WHERE THE *WOLFRIDERS* ARE--

-- IF THE WOLFRIDERS *LIVE*!

THEY LIVE, NIGHTFALL! IF THEY WERE DEAD, WE'D *FEEL* IT!

COME ON! WE'LL RUN LIKE *DEER* AND REACH BLUE MOUNTAIN BEFORE THE NIGHT'S HALF DONE!

:PANT PANT: CUTTER! W-WAIT--

I-I CAN'T--!

WITHOUT BREAKING STRIDE, CUTTER SWEEPS LEETAH ONTO WOODSHAVER'S BACK!

NOW, MY GENTLE *LEETAH*--

--BE A *WOLFRIDER*!

THEY CALL THEMSELVES THE *HOAN G'TAY SHO* WHICH MEANS "FAVORED OF THOSE WHO DWELL ON HIGH." **NONNA**, THE SYMBOL-MAKER, WAS ONCE A MEMBER OF THIS TRIBE, BEFORE HER MATE, **ADAR**, TOOK HER TO LIVE IN HIS OWN LAND. **NONNA'S** DEPARTURE CHANGED NOTHING, FOR NOTHING CAN SWAY THE **HOAN G'TAY SHO** FROM THEIR LONG CHOSEN PATH.

THE PIPES CALL LIKE THIN-THROATED BIRDS TO THOSE WHO DWELL HIGH ABOVE--

--TELLING THEM OF AN *OFFERING* SOON TO ASCEND THE MOUNTAINSIDE.

ONE-EYE SPIES UPON THE HUMANS, UNAWARE THAT *HE* IS THE CAUSE OF THEIR PURPOSEFUL ACTIONS.

OUR LAST GIFT TO THE BIRD SPIRITS WAS ONE OF **OLD AGE.** TWO OF OUR ELDEST TRIBEFOLK CLIMBED THE STEEP PATH TO SPEND THE LIFE LEFT TO THEM WITH THE HONORED ONES.

THE IMMORTAL BIRD SPIRITS WOULD KNOW US IN EVERY ASPECT AND CONDITION OF OUR BEING.

THEREFORE WE SEND THEM, NOW, A GIFT OF *BEAUTY* IN ALL ITS FULLNESS.

MAY THE HONORED ONES' MESSENGER, SILENT FOR THREE DAYS, KNOW BY THIS OFFERING THAT WE AWAIT HIS WORD!

THIS COULD BE MY ONLY CHANCE!

I'LL BET THAT *CAVE* IS AN ENTRANCE INTO THE MOUNTAIN! LOOKS LIKE IT'S WIDE OPEN TO THE HUMANS' USE... THAT MEANS IT'S WIDE OPEN TO *ME!*

MAYBE *I* CAN'T SCARE ALL THOSE *BIRD-RIDERS* BY MYSELF...

7

BUT WITH A PACK OF ANGRY *WOLVES* AT MY SIDE -- HAH! THAT'LL MAKE 'EM THINK TWICE ABOUT HOLDING THE WOLF-RIDERS PRISONERS!

ALL WE HAVE TO DO IS SCARE THE HUMANS ENOUGH TO GET PAST 'EM!

EH? WHAT'S UP?

RUFF R-R-RUFF!

WHINE

ONE-EYE KNOWS BETTER THAN TO IGNORE THE WOLVES, NO MATTER HOW URGENT THE NEED TO PUT HIS DARING PLAN INTO ACTION.

INSTINCTIVELY HE TILTS HIS HEAD BACK AND CALLS.

ALMOST AT ONCE AN ANSWERING HOWL WAFTS UP FROM THE VALLEY.

AYOOOOOOOAH!

BY *TWO-SPEAR'S* STONE POINTS!

THEY'RE ALIVE!

ALIVE!

ONE-EYE!

SO HE'S THE MISSING ONE!

HA HAH! CURSE YOUR WAYWARD RUMPS, YOU FOOLHEADED CUBS!

SO! YOU TWO SURVIVED YOUR MAD QUEST AFTER ALL!

SO FAR!

AND *YOU* WEREN'T CAPTURED BY THE GIANT BIRDS!

HUNH! NOT FOR LACK OF *TRYING*!

ONE OF 'EM GRABBED *CLEARBROOK*, SO I GRABBED *HER*.

BUT THAT OVERGROWN SQUIRREL-HAWK WAS SO STRONG, HE FLEW OFF WITH *BOTH* OF US!

CRASH!

MY WEIGHT MADE 'IM FLY LOW, AND THAT WAS TOO BAD FOR ME!

I WOKE UP A LONG TIME LATER TO THE WOLVES HOWLING 'ROUND THE BASE OF THE TREE.

THE WOLF-RIDERS...

THEY'RE BEING HELD UP THERE ON THAT MOUNTAIN?

IN IT, LAD!

MOUNTAIN'S *HOLLOW*!

THAT MUCH I LEARNED FROM MY ONE SENDING TO *CLEAR-BROOK*!

NO! DON'T TRY TO SEND— ANY OF YOU!!

THE "BAD ONE" MUSTN'T LEARN--

--HOW MANY OF US ARE STILL FREE.

THE "BAD ONE?"

SHHH! WE'VE GOT EVEN *MORE* TROUBLE!

CAREFULLY THE ELVES CREEP TO A VANTAGE WHERE THEY CAN OBSERVE, UNSEEN, THE STRANGE CEREMONY OF THE HUMANS.

SKYWISE, LOOK! IT'S NONNA'S TRIBE!

SEE HOW THEY'RE DRESSED?

I DO!

WE CAN ENTER THE MOUNTAIN THROUGH THAT *TUNNEL* UP THERE.

BUT FIRST WE'LL HAVE TO FIGHT OUR WAY PAST THOSE CURSED ROUND-EARS!

MAYBE NOT! WATCH THIS!

WHA—?!! GET BACK HERE!!

9

HE'S WALKING RIGHT UP TO THEM!?

THEY'LL *KILL* HIM!

I-I DON'T BELIEVE IT! THE HUMANS...

THEY'RE *BOWING!*

AT THE SAME TIME, WITHIN THE MOUNTAIN...

HEAR THE *PIPES!*

I WONDER WHAT *PETS* THE HUMANS SEND ME NOW.

I WONDER THAT YOU NEVER TIRE OF TOYING WITH THE FIVE FINGERED ONES!

AREN'T THESE SLAVES WHO CALL THEM- SELVES *WOLF RIDERS* MORE AMUSING?

SIGH: OUR SAVAGE LITTLE COUSINS ARE TOO EASILY UNDERSTOOD...TOO MUCH LIKE OURSELVES DESPITE THEIR BESTIAL TRAITS.

I AM, AS YOU KNOW, MOST FOND OF SURPRISES.

BUT THE HUMANS ARE ENDLESSLY INTERESTING TO ME.

JUST WHEN I THINK I'VE OBSERVED EVERY POSSIBLE TRICK OF THEIR BEHAVIOR--

--THEY SURPRISE ME ANEW.

10

11

12

13

LISTEN, *FEATHER-ROBE*... QUIT INTERFERING! I *MEAN* IT!

I BELIEVE YOU DO, SAVAGE..!

I BELIEVE YOU DO!

FREE, NOW, TO SEEK OUT THEIR TRIBEFOLK IN THE CAVERNOUS LAIR OF THE BIRD SPIRITS, THE WOLFRIDERS SEND FORTH THEIR CALL.

TREESTUMP!

PLASH!

PIKE!

SCOUTER! DEWSHINE!

14

CLEARBROOK!

STRONGBOW! MOONSHADE!

:GASP:

IT'S *CUTTER!* HE'S *HERE!*

HE'S HERE!

AYOOOAH!

THERE'S MY CUB, FIT AND FINE AS EVER!

CUTTER! OH CUTTER! THEY'VE PUT STRONGBOW IN A CAGE!

WHAT--?

MAKE THEM SET HIM FREE!

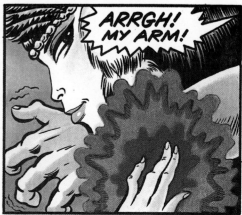

ARRGH! MY ARM!

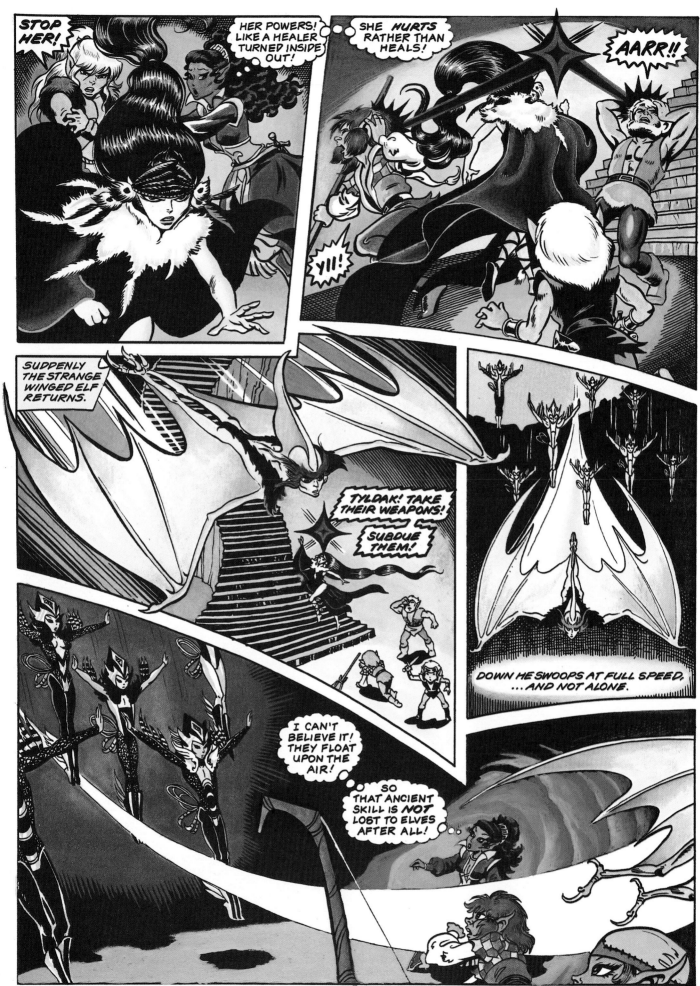

17

UNH!

BRIERSTING! GO!!

TREESTUMP, LOOK OUT!

WHA—?

THE WARNING COMES A MOMENT TOO LATE.

KEEP THAT BLADE WHIRLING, LAD!

I'LL BE OUT OF THIS IN NO TIME!

IT GOES BADLY!

THE SAVAGES FIGHT AS THOUGH IT IS ALL THEY HAVE EVER DONE!

BUT I KNOW HOW TO TIP THE BALANCE!

THE COWARD! SHE'S GOING AFTER STRONGBOW!

19

WOLFRIDERS! DO AS CUTTER SAYS! FORGET ABOUT ME!

STRONG-BOW!

NO!

THIS IS MERELY A REMINDER.

I HAVE THE POWER TO *SHATTER* YOUR FRIEND FROM WITHIN!

PROVOKE ME FURTHER--

--AND I WILL *DO* IT!

SH-SHE'S NOT LYING! WHAT CAN WE DO?

THIS IS WHY WE DIDN'T DARE REBEL BEFORE, LAD.

THAT *WINNOWILL* HOLDS *STRONG-BOW'S* LIFE IN HER HANDS!

WINNOWILL...

WITHOUT WARNING *LEETAH* DASHES TOWARD THE ELFIN ARCHER'S CELL.

STRONGBOW!

TAKE MY HAND!

20

THERE!

SHE CANNOT HURT YOU NOW!

HMMM...

MARVELOUS!

AN ELEGANT DISPLAY!

I SEE YOUR DISSIMILARITY TO YOUR COMPANIONS IS MORE THAN SKIN DEEP, MY DEAR.

WHY HAVE YOU ABUSED AND HUMILIATED THE WOLFRIDERS?

WHY HAVE YOU TAKEN AWAY THEIR FREEDOM?

BECAUSE *THEY* HAVE TAKEN THE LIFE OF A *FLEDGELING*-- A DESTINED BOND-BIRD OF THE *GLIDERS!*

THESE ATE OF ITS FLESH.

BUT *THAT* ONE SHOT THE FLEDGELING DOWN!

IT IS A CRIME FOR WHICH THEY MUST *PAY!*

WE WERE GIVEN A CHOICE... SERVE THE *GLIDERS* AS SLAVES, OR TAKE OUR FREEDOM IN EXCHANGE FOR *STRONGBOW!*

THAT'S *NO* CHOICE, *TREESTUMP!*

YOU DID THE ONLY THING YOU COULD. BUT IT'S *OVER* NOW.

WE'RE GETTING *OUT* OF HERE! *ALL* OF US!

MY, MY! HOW OUR SCATTERED DESCENDANTS HAVE DEGENERATED!

NOT ONLY HAVE THEIR BODIES SHRUNK--

--THEIR SENSE OF HONOR SEEMS TO HAVE VANISHED COMPLETELY!

YOU, LITTLE CHIEFTAIN... *JUSTICE* IS MERELY A MATTER OF CONVENIENCE TO YOU, IS IT NOT?

WHAT'RE YOU TALK-ING ABOUT?

IF SOMEONE KILLED ONE OF YOUR WOLF-FRIENDS, WHAT WOULD YOU DO?

WHY, I'D *K--!*

UH...

THAT WOULD DEPEND..!

CUTTER SENSES A TRAP.

YOU WASTE MY TIME, *FEATHER-ROBE!*

I'LL TAKE THIS UP WITH YOUR *CHIEF* AND NO ONE ELSE!

WITH MY... *CHIEF?*

HOW QUAINTLY YOU PUT IT!

BY ALL MEANS LET US SET THIS MATTER BEFORE *VOLL, LORD* OF THE *GLIDERS.*

CUTTER?

HMM?

I THINK WE'RE UP TO OUR EARS IN BIRD PL--

--UH HUH!

WELL, *TAM*...YOU FOUND WHAT YOU HOPED YOU'D FIND. THE "BIRD SPIRITS" *ARE* ELVES.

BUT *SUNTOP'S* WARNING WAS WELL WORTH HEEDING.

THERE'S SOMETHING *WRONG* WITH THIS PLACE--

--AND WITH THESE FOLK WHO CALL THEM-SELVES *GLIDERS!*

I'M GLAD *SUNTOP* AND *EMBER* ARE SAFE IN THE WOODS WITH *REDLANCE.*

DON'T SEND ANY MORE! THAT PRYING SHE-FERRET CAN PICK YOUR THOUGHTS RIGHT OUT OF THE AIR!

LED BY *WINNOWILL*, THE WOLFRIDERS VENTURE DEEP INTO *THE BOWELS* OF THE *GLIDERS'* MOUNTAIN DOMAIN.

POOR LITTLE *PETALWING!* IT MUST BE *LOST* SOMEWHERE IN THIS HUGE, CONFUSING PLACE!

DEEPER...

I'LL TELL YOU ONE THING-- THE TROLL CAVES WERE NEVER *THIS* FANCY!

AND DEEPER STILL...

JOYLEAF... LET YOUR BLOOD FLOW STRONGER IN ME, NOW, THAN *BEARCLAW'S.*

KEEP ME CALM AND WISE BEFORE THIS *LORD VOLL.*

IT'S TIME TO *THINK,* NOT TO FIGHT!

ONE-EYE!

CLEARBROOK!

THEY KEPT ME FROM GOING TO YOU!

THEY TIED MY HANDS AND FEET!

BY THE TWO MOONS!

WHAT HAVE THEY *DONE* TO YOU —?!

:CHUCKLE: NOTHING, BELOVED! *NOTHING!*

THERE SITS *LORD VOLL*, LITTLE CHIEFTAIN.

CONVINCE *HIM* OF YOUR TRIBE'S INNOCENCE —

—IF YOU CAN.

24

BOLDLY *CUTTER* STEPS TO THE FOOT OF *VOLL'S* ELABORATE PERCH. THE TWO LEADERS EYE EACH OTHER COOLLY.

I AM *CUTTER,* CHIEF OF THE WOLFRIDERS.

I DEMAND THAT YOU RELEASE *STRONG-BOW* AND LET ME AND MY TRIBE GO IN PEACE.

HE SEEMS EVEN OLDER THAN *SAVAH!*

A CLOAK MADE OF SO MANY YEARS MUST WEIGH HEAVILY ON HIM...

HE WEARS IT WITHOUT JOY!

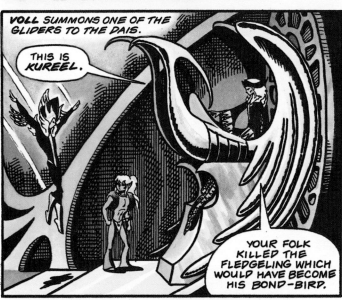

VOLL SUMMONS ONE OF THE GLIDERS TO THE DAIS.

THIS IS *KUREEL.*

YOUR FOLK KILLED THE FLEDGELING WHICH WOULD HAVE BECOME HIS BOND-BIRD.

I'M SORRY FOR THAT. WE'RE *HUNTERS.*

STRONGBOW SHOT THE BIRD DOWN FOR FOOD.

HE DIDN'T KNOW.

THE *CHOSEN EIGHT* WHO RIDE THE GREAT BIRDS ARE HUNTERS TOO.

AND WAIT LONGER STILL, UNTIL HIS NEW MOUNT IS FULL-FLEDGED AND READY TO FLY THE HUNT.

BUT *KUREEL* MUST WAIT, NOW, FOR THE NEXT HATCHING.

THEN LET MY TRIBE GO--

AND *WE'LL* BRING YOU MEAT TO MAKE UP FOR THE BIRD'S DEATH.

THAT HARDLY SEEMS ADEQUATE ATONEMENT, *LORD VOLL...*

I WOULD SAY THAT A LIFE FOR A LIFE IS MORE IN ORDER!

25

I AGREE!

YOU WON'T KILL *STRONGBOW!*

THAT WAS NEVER MY INTENTION, YOUTH.

BUT THE ARCHER'S WOLF-FRIEND...

≥GASP≤ *BRIERSTING?!*

NO!

A LIFE FOR A LIFE... IT IS ONLY *JUST.*

MY MOUNT WAS SLAIN WHILE TRYING ITS WINGS!

WHY SHOULD THE *KILLER'S* MOUNT LIVE?

BECAUSE IT WAS AN ACCIDENT!

WHY WON'T YOU *LISTEN?*

LORD VOLL, PLEASE! YOU CANNOT COMMAND US TO KILL THE WOLF!

LEETAH!

YOU MIGHT AS WELL COMMAND THAT WE PUT OUR OWN *CHILDREN* TO DEATH!

WHAT?!

COME HERE!

LORD VOLL'S MELANCHOLY EYES FIX STERNLY, WONDERINGLY UPON *LEETAH'S* DARK-SKINNED BEAUTY. HIS THROAT TIGHTENS AS HE SPEAKS.

CHILDREN, YOU SAY?

I THOUGHT ONLY *WINNOWILL* WAS CAPABLE OF SUCH CRUEL MOCKERY.

26

THERE ARE NO MORE CHILDREN!

THERE WILL *BE* NO MORE!

WE ARE ALL *DYING* WITHIN THIS MOUNTAIN... DYING, THOUGH UNABLE TO DIE!

SURELY YOU HAVE SEEN THAT!

DESPITE THE RECENT BATTLE, LEETAH'S HEART IS TOUCHED BY THE AGED LEADER'S PAIN.

BUT THERE *ARE* ELF CHILDREN IN THE WORLD, *LORD VOLL!*

LITTLE ONES FULL OF STRENGTH AND PROMISE...

LITTLE ONES WHO HAVE KNOWN ONLY RESPECT AND LOVE ALL THEIR SHORT LIVES.

IF ONLY THAT WERE TRUE...

AFTER ALL THIS TIME...

I'D GIVE *ANY-THING* TO GAZE INTO THE EYES OF A CHILD--

"--JUST ONCE...TO FEEL HOPE AGAIN!"

OH, *SUNTOP!* DON'T BE SUCH AN OLD *GLOOMER.*

I DIDN'T DO IT *RIGHT!* I DIDN'T WARN FATHER THE WAY *SAVAH* WANTED ME TO!

NOW HE'S UP IN THE MOUNTAIN WHERE HE ISN'T SUPPOSED TO BE!

AWW...

FATHER WILL SAVE THE WOLFRIDERS!

HE CAN DO EVERY- THING!

NO ONE CAN DO "EVERYTHING" BY HIM- SELF, *EMBER.* BUT WITH THE WOLF- RIDERS FIGHTING BY HIS SIDE --

--THERE'S VERY LITTLE YOUR FATHER *CAN'T* DO!

OH, LOOK!!

TIMMORN'S BLOOD!

GIANT BIRDS!

HIDE IN THE BUSHES, *QUICK!*

CRACKLE

REDLANCE!

EH?!

NO NEED FOR WARINESS, BELOVED.

I RIDE THE WIND ASTRIDE THIS GREAT BIRD!

NIGHTFALL! IT'S *NIGHTFALL!*

HA HAH!

MEET US AT OUR LANDING PLACE!

BRING *SUNTOP* AND *EMBER!*

THEY ARE *NEEDED!*

28

MOTHER! FATHER! DID YOU *SEE?* DID YOU SEE US FLY UP IN THE AIR?

WE SAW, EMBER!

FATHER! YOU'RE ALL RIGHT!

EVERYBODY'S ALL RIGHT!

IN THEIR EXCITEMENT, *SUNTOP* AND *EMBER* DO NOT NOTICE HOW THE GLIDERS STARE AT THEM WITH ENVY-TINGED YEARNING.

THE BIG BIRD TOOK US UP SO *HIGH*— WE SAW ALL THE HUMANS AND THEY WERE SMALL LIKE LITTLE SPECKS AND...

...GOT MY "MAGIC FEELING, MOTHER, BUT I'M NOT SCARED LIKE BEFORE.

WHO'S *HE?*

THIS IS *LORD VOLL*... A *FRIEND!*

YOU LOOK LIKE A *FUNNY OLD BIRD!*

HEY!

EMBER! HE'S LIKE *SAVAH!* BE POLITE!

BAP!

WELL, LORD VOLL..?

YOU DID NOT... LIE!

NOW YOU WILL SEE THAT *MY* WORD IS EQUALLY HONORABLE.

STIFFLY, HIS RAGE AND HUMILIATION BARELY CONTAINED, A NEWLY-FREED *STRONGBOW* STRIDES INTO THE AERIE.

ONLY *BRIERSTING'S* HAPPY GREETING IS NOT DAMPENED BY THE TENSION IN THE AIR.

CUTTER, YOUR CHILDREN HAVE WON FREEDOM FOR YOU AND YOUR TRIBE.

THE CHOSEN EIGHT WILL TRANSPORT EACH OF YOU DOWN TO THE GROUND IF YOU WISH.

BUT I WANT --

--I *ASK* THAT YOU STAY.

THE FLEDGELING'S DEATH WAS WORTHWHILE, FOR BY LUCKY CIRCUMSTANCE IT HAS BROUGHT ME THIS *PROOF* OF OUR RACE'S RENEWAL!

I CAN'T SPEAK FOR MY TRIBE WITHOUT FIRST HOLDING COUNCIL, LORD *VOLL.*

BUT FOR MYSELF, I WOULD CHOOSE TO STAY AND LEARN ALL I COULD OF THE GLIDERS.

THE WISEST ELF I KNOW ONCE SAID THAT OUR RACE IS OF "ONE HEART AND ONE MIND!

I BELIEVE WE SHOULD ALL BE *TOGETHER!* IT'S MY DREAM TO FIND AND UNITE *ALL* THE LOST CHILDREN OF THE *HIGH ONES.*

THEN LOOK NO FURTHER, LITTLE CHIEFTAIN.

YOUR QUEST IS *DONE.*

WE *ARE* THE *HIGH ONES!*

32

34

35

ELSEWHERE...

LET PETAL-WING OUT!! LET PETAL-WING OUT!!

SUNNYGOLD HIGHTHING BE NICE! OPEN CAGE!

PETALWING GO FETCH BEESWEETS TO TWINE IN SOFT PRETTY HAIR!

AWWWW... LET PETAL-WING OUT!

I'D LIKE TO.

BUT YOUR CAGE HAS NO DOOR.

THE BARS ARE STONE AND I MIGHT HURT YOU IF I TRY TO BREAK THEM.

YES! GO ON! SMASH! SMASH!

THEY'RE COMING!

PETAL-WING STRONG!

HURRY! HURRY!

SHHH!

--FORTUNATE YOU CAPTURED THE PRESERVER BEFORE ANYONE — ESPECIALLY LORD VOLL — CAUGHT SIGHT OF IT.

THE WRETCHED LITTLE PEST SPAT ITS WEBS IN MY EYES... NEARLY SENT ME FLYING INTO A WALL!

BUT WHY ARE YOU SO EAGER TO KEEP THE PRESERVER HIDDEN?

BECAUSE LORD VOLL GROWS RESTLESS AND DISCONTENT.

HE DWELLS TOO MUCH UPON HIS MEMORIES.

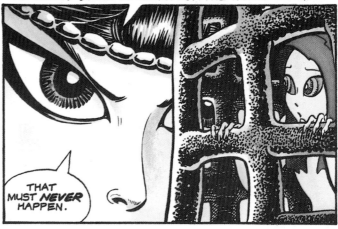

IF HE WERE TO SEE THE PRESERVER NOW, HIS THOUGHTS WOULD LEAP FROM THE PAST TO THE FUTURE. HE WOULD BEGIN TO YEARN FOR THE WORLD OUTSIDE.

THAT MUST NEVER HAPPEN.

WHEN THEY WERE SLAVES, AND FEWER IN NUMBER, I COULD KEEP THE WOLFRIDERS UNDER CONTROL.

BUT THIS *CUTTER*, HIS *LITTER* AND HIS CURSED *QUEST* WILL DISRUPT EVERYTHING--

--UNLESS I CAN GET THEM ALL OUT OF H--?!

HMM...

SO, SHE RUNS LOOSE IN YOUR CHAMBERS NOW, *TYLDAK*?

YOU ARE A TOLERANT MASTER.

I DO NOT OWN HER!

I WOULD NOT!

SHE IS NO PART OF ME!

THEN DO WHAT YOU *MUST* WITH HER AND BE *RID* OF HER!

FURTHER DELAY WILL MAKE YOU *ILL*!

JUST THEN--

DEWSHINE!

FATHER..! AND THE OTHERS!

THEY'RE CALLING *COUNCIL*!

THE SLENDER WOLFRIDER HESITATES, TORN BETWEEN HER TRIBE'S INSISTANT SENDING AND ANOTHER, EVEN MORE URGENT, CALL.

FINALLY...

NO ONE OWNS ME!!

I'M A *WOLFRIDER*!

HA HA HA HA!

I--I'M *FREE*!

AT **LORD VOLL'S** COMMAND SEVERAL OF THE GLIDERS ESCORT THE WOLFRIDERS TO A TORCHLIT GROTTO.

THE GENTLE SPLASHING OF SMALL WATERFALLS INVITES THE FOREST ELVES, FOR THE FIRST TIME IN DAYS, TO TAKE THEIR EASE.

MAGIC! EVERYTHING HERE HAS **MAGIC** IN IT!

MANY OF THE GLIDERS ARE ROCK-SHAPERS, CUB. THEY SHAPED THIS ENTIRE MOUNTAIN TO SUIT THEIR FANCY.

(GRUMBLE) THEY CAN'T LEAVE WELL ENOUGH ALONE!

GIVE ME A TREE TO SHAPE ANY DAY! ROCKS DON'T BREATHE!

FATHER..?

TREESTUMP'S EYES LIGHT UP AS HIS DAUGHTER SHYLY COMES TO HIM.

PRETTY CUB, I MISSED YOU! WE **ALL** DID! WHY..?

PLEASE, FATHER...

JUST LET ME SIT QUIETLY WITH YOU.

38

UH... WELL, LAD, YOU WERE RIGHT! THERE *ARE* OTHER ELVES IN THE WORLD BE- SIDES THE SUN FOLK.

BUT THESE AREN'T JUST ELVES. THEY CLAIM TO BE THE *HIGH ONES!*

HAH!

AND *I'M* AN EIGHT LEGGED TREEWEE WITH *BLUE FUR!*

WE DON'T KNOW ENOUGH ABOUT THE GLIDERS TO TELL TRUE FROM FALSE.

WE KNOW ABOUT *WINNOWILL!*

STRONGBOW, DON'T *SEND!* REMEMBER...

YOU THINK *I* CARE?

I *WANT* HER TO KNOW MY HATE! IF SHE'S SPYING, I HOPE SHE GETS A *HEAD-FULL!*

KNOW WHAT *I* THINK? *LORD VOLL* LOOKS OLD ENOUGH TO BE ONE OF THE *FIRST* OF OUR KIND.

I TRUST *WINNOWILL* ABOUT AS MUCH AS I'D TRUST A *GRINNING TROLL!*

BUT FOR ALL WE KNOW--

-- SHE MIGHT JUST BE TELLING THE TRUTH.

THE GLIDERS *COULD* BE THE *HIGH ONES!*

FOR ALL WE KNOW...

SO WHAT IF THEY ARE? SHOULD WE, THEN, BECOME LIKE THOSE FOOL HUMANS WHO WORSHIP THE GLIDERS AND SING THEIR PRAISES EVERY NIGHT? DO WE STAY HERE AND SERVE *LORD VOLL* HAND AND FOOT? DO WE END UP AS *WINNOWILL'S PETS?*

WHAT ARE WE BECOMING?

EVER SINCE THE HOLT BURNED DOWN WE'VE BEEN FORGETTING *"THE WAY."*

THE FIRE DIDN'T CHANGE *EVERYTHING*, DID IT? WE'RE *STILL* THE WOLFRIDERS!

WE CAN RETURN TO "THE WAY" AND START A *NEW* HOLT -- BUT NOT IF WE STAY HERE!

STRONGBOW'S IMPASSIONED PLEA STIRS DEEP NOSTALGIA IN HIS PEOPLE'S HEARTS...

I *DO* REMEMBER THOSE GOOD DAYS... AND I'D GO BACK IF I COULD. BUT I CAN'T BELIEVE THE QUEST ENDS WITH THE GLIDERS, NO MATTER WHAT *THEY* SAY.

IF ONLY THINGS *COULD* BE THE WAY THEY WERE... BUT SOME OF US HAVE CHANGED--

--INSIDE.

(YAWN) THIS IS TOO MUCH *THINKING* FOR ME! MY HEAD'S SO FULL-- --I CAN HARDLY HOLD IT UP!

BY GOODTREE'S REST! I'M TIRED TOO!

YOUR CUBS HAVE THE RIGHT IDEA!

FLAP FLAP FLAP

EH?

A FLUTTERING OF LONG, LEATHERN WINGS HERALDS THE SUDDEN ARRIVAL OF TYLDAK.

LIKE A CURVED ARROW IN ITS FLIGHT HE SWERVES--

--THROUGH HIGH ARCHWAYS AND AROUND LACY COLUMNS LEADING TO THE GROTTO.

GET OUT OF HERE, YOU WINGED BUNDLE OF STICKS!

QUIT IT, PIKE!

WE DON'T HAVE THE RIGHT!

41

IS IT--

--RECOGNITION?

TREESTUMP! YOU MEAN IT'S REALLY *TRUE?* DEWSHINE AND THAT -- THAT *BIRD ELF* ARE --?

AYE... I'M AFRAID SO! IT'S A MISMATCH IF EVER I SAW ONE, BUT WHAT CAN I -- WHAT CAN *ANYONE* DO?

RECOGNITION IS RECOGNITION!

IT'S *WRONG!*

TYLDAK TREATS HER LIKE SHE'S *LESS THAN NOTHING!*

AND SHE FEELS --

-- ASHAMED! LIKE SHE ISN'T ONE OF *US* ANY MORE!

(GROAN) POOR LITTLE COUSIN!

SHE'S IN A BIGGER MESS --

-- THAN *LEETAH* AND I WERE IN WHEN *WE* RECOGNIZED!

WORN OUT BY TOO MANY PROBLEMS, THE WOLFRIDERS BREAK COUNCIL TO REST A WHILE. BUT LEETAH IS TOO TROUBLED TO JOIN THEM.

DEWSHINE...

THE WAY SHE LOOKED AT ME...

AS THOUGH PLEADING FOR HELP!

BRRR! THIS PLACE IS SO COLD AND DARK!

HOW I MISS THE SUN!

EVEN *PETALWING'S* SINGING WOULD BRIGHTEN THESE GLOOMY HALLS!

WHERE CAN MY LITTLE FRIEND BE?

HELLO, DOOR!

CAN YOU TELL ME WHERE *TYLDAK* AND *DEWSHINE* ARE..?

SEND IF YOU CANNOT SPEAK!

MOMENTS PASS AS *LEETAH* AWAITS A RESPONSE.

BUT NO ANSWER COMES.

STRANGE! I'M NOT SURE *DOOR* EVEN KNEW I WAS THERE!

HAS SHE SENT HER SPIRIT OUT—-THE WAY *SAVAH* DID?

NOW WHO IS *THIS?*

HELLO!

I AM SEARCHING FOR *DEWSHINE.*

CAN YOU——?!

GREAT SUN!!

HE BREATHES. HIS HEART BEATS. BUT OTHERWISE HE'S AS STILL AS—-

——*DEATH!*

JUST LIKE *DOOR!*

HE IS CALLED *BRACE.*

GASP!

THERE IS A WEAKNESS IN THE STONE OF THIS ARCH-WAY. *BRACE* PREVENTS ITS CERTAIN COLLAPSE.

HE IS A ROCK-SHAPER, ATTUNED TO MINUTE SHIFTS OF STRESS WHICH HE CORRECTS.

AND THAT IS... ALL HE DOES?!

OF COURSE!

ARE YOU LOST, MY DEAR?

ALLOW ME TO GUIDE YOU.

I HOPED FOR THE OPPORTUNITY TO SPEAK WITH YOU, AWAY FROM YOUR LESS... *UNDERSTANDING* COMPANIONS.

CAN YOU BLAME THEM? YOU TREATED THEM CRUELLY. ESPECIALLY *STRONGBOW!*

THAT IS A MATTER OF OPINION.

BUT I HAVE BEEN THINKING.

YOUR YOUNG LIFEMATE HAS A GRANDIOSE DREAM--

--"TO FIND AND UNITE ALL THE LOST CHILDREN OF THE *HIGH ONES.*"

I TRUST HE HAS FINALLY REALIZED THAT THERE *ARE* NO OTHER ELVES TO BE FOUND--

--THAT HE CAN GO HOME *FULFILLED,* NOW THAT HIS QUEST IS FINISHED.

HOW CAN YOU BE SO *SURE?*

HA HA HA HA!

BECAUSE WE ARE THE *HIGH* ONES, MY DEAR, AND WE HAVE BEEN *EXPECTING* YOU FOR SOME TIME!

HERE IN THIS MOUNTAIN WE HAVE PRESERVED OUR WAY OF LIFE JUST AS IT WAS--

--BEFORE THAT TERRIBLE ACCIDENT, LONG AGO, SCATTERED US OVER ALIEN SOIL!

CONSIDERING HOW HARSHLY THE WORLD OUTSIDE HAS DEALT WITH THEM, WE CAN *FORGIVE* THE WOLF-RIDERS THEIR MURDEROUS SAVAGERY.

BUT YOU, *LEETAH,* OBVIOUSLY REPRESENT THE FAR LESS "DAMAGED" GROUP.

WHERE DO *YOUR* PEOPLE DWELL, LOVELY ONE?

IN THE DESERT! WE ARE CALLED THE *SUN FOLK.*

SAVAH, OUR MOTHER OF MEMORY, IS MUCH LIKE YOUR *LORD VOLL!*

SHE IS VERY WISE AND HAS MANY OF THE OLD POWERS!

INDEED!

YOU DESCRIBE HER SO WELL--

--THAT IT SEEMS SHE HAS *TOUCHED* ME...LIKE THE FLUTTERING OF A MOTH'S WING!

TELL ME... *CUTTER'S* QUEST--

--WAS IT *YOUR* QUEST TOO?

I CHOOSE TO BE WITH HIM-- WHEREVER HE GOES.

WELL SAID! THOUGH YOU WOULD FIT IN WELL HERE, I FORSEE THAT YOU WILL GO WITH THE WOLFRIDERS--

--WHEN THEY DECIDE TO RETURN TO THE FOREST.

EVEN DEWSHINE WILL LEAVE--

"--WHEN SHE AND TYLDAK HAVE ANSWERED THE DEMANDS OF RECOGNITION!"

BUT--

--BUT TYLDAK! HE'S - HE'S SO--

DO NOT INTERFERE WITH THEM.

--DIFFERENT? ONLY IN APPEARANCE. I ASSURE YOU HIS BLOOD IS AS PURE AS LORD VOLL'S HIMSELF.

TYLDAK WAS NOT ALWAYS AS YOU SEE HIM NOW.

"I GAVE HIM HIS WINGS BECAUSE HE BEGGED ME TO."

"I DREW THEM FROM THE VERY SUBSTANCE OF HIS BODY--"

"--SO THAT HE COULD SOAR THROUGH THE SKY AS FREELY AS THE GREAT BIRDS!"

46

DO NOT BE SHOCKED.

HEALING...ROCK SHAPING... IT IS ALL ONE.

FLESH CAN BE MOLDED AS EASILY AS STONE.

YOU OUGHT TO TRY IT, MY DEAR.

YOU'LL BE AMAZED AT YOUR OWN VERSATILITY.

AH! FINISHED SO SOON?

IT IS A SIMPLE DESIGN, AS YOU REQUESTED, WINNOWILL.

THIS IS A GIFT FOR CUTTER. AS CHIEF OF HIS TRIBE, HE IS DUE SOME TOKEN OF RESPECT.

BESIDES, I CONFESS THAT HIS ABILITY TO DREAM IMPRESSES ME.

IT SETS HIM WELL APART FROM HIS FOLLOWERS.

GIVE THE GIFT TO HIM... WITH MY APOLOGIES FOR ANY EARLIER --UNDUE --VIOLENCE.

.....THANK YOU.

DAZZLED, BUT NOT TOTALLY CONVINCED, LEETAH MAKES HER WAY BACK TO THE GROTTO.

LEETAH! WHERE'VE YOU BEEN?

WHAT'S THAT YOU'VE GOT THERE?

LATER, AFTER THE HEALER HAS TOLD OF HER ENCOUNTER WITH WINNOWILL...

HMPH! SHE DIDN'T GIVE YOU A MOMENT TO THINK, DID SHE?

NO...BUT I THOUGHT ANYWAY.

I'M STILL THINKING.

AHHH!

WELL... AT LEAST IT FITS.

YOUR OLD LEATHERS *WERE* WORN THIN WITH TRAVEL.

MMM... THIS IS THE SOFTEST, SLEEKEST FUR I HAVE EVER TOUCHED!

AND THE FEATHERS--

--WHITE AS *CLOUDS!*

WHITE AS *SNOW!*

(GIGGLE) WHAT *IS* SNOW?

(SIGH) I WISH I COULD DO THAT.

DO YOU?

YOU SEEM TOO SQUAT AND CLUMSY!

THAT SO?

WATCH--

--THIS!

THUMP!

HA HAH!

WUMP!

:CHUCKLE:

48

WHAT'S YOUR NAME?

ARÓREE.

I AM ONE OF THE *CHOSEN EIGHT.*

I REMEMBER! I THINK YOU CLIPPED ME WITH THAT BIRDCLAW WEAPON OF YOURS DURING THE FIGHT.

THIS IS A *TALON-WHIP.*

I USE IT TO SNATCH UP SMALL GAME WHEN I HUNT.

YOU FLY ONE OF THE GIANT BIRDS.

I *ENVY* YOU! YOU CAN GET CLOSER TO THE SKY THAN *I* EVER COULD--

--EVEN IF I CLIMBED THE TALLEST MOUNTAIN!

IT MUST REALLY BE SOMETHING TO REACH UP AND TOUCH THE STARS!

I LIKE THE WAY YOUR EYES SHINE WHEN YOU SPEAK. THEY ARE LIKE STARS THEMSELVES.

WHAT ARE *YOU* CALLED?

SKYWISE...

AND ARE YOU WISE..?

...ABOUT THE SKY?

ABOUT *MANY* THINGS.

SHALL WE SEE?

SHORTLY...

WHEEEEE ET!

SKREEEAAAWW!

SKAAAWWW!

HELLO, LITTLETRILL, MY FRIEND!

THIS IS *NOT* WHAT I HAD IN MIND!

49

ALMOST CASUALLY, **ARDREE** FLOATS UP TO MEET HER BOND BIRD, SETTLING ON ITS GILDED HARNESS WITH WEIGHTLESS EASE.

THEY CIRCLE BLUE MOUNTAIN'S PEAK--

--AND RETURN MUCH TOO QUICKLY FOR--

SKYWISE!

JUMP!

"JUMP" SHE WANTS!

WE'LL CATCH YOU!

OH... PUCKERNUUUTS!

OOF!

WHISTLING AND BITING, THE ENVIOUS WIND BUFFETS THE AIRBORNE ELVES.

SKYWISE HANGS ON FOR DEAR LIFE!

OPEN YOUR EYES, WOLFRIDER!

LOOK DOWN!

=ULP=

THERE IS MUCH TO SEE!

"MUCH TO SEE..." AND MUCH TO FEEL; FOR SUDDENLY THIS WORLD-WITHOUT-A-NAME WILL NEVER SEEM THE SAME TO SKYWISE AGAIN.

SUDDENLY THE WORLD IS BOTH LARGER AND SMALLER THAN THE STARGAZER EVER REALIZED. AND THE **ORDER** OF IT ALL, SEEN FROM ABOVE, IS A REVELATION.

FIRST WE SHALL GIVE THE HUMANS A SMALL GIFT!

WH—WHEN DID YOU MAKE FRIENDS WITH THEM, AROREE?

"OH, LONG AGO," LAUGHS THE GLIDER.

"THEY MAKE THEIR HOMES NEAR US BECAUSE THEY LOVE US! WINNOWILL FINDS THEM AMUSING. SO DO I."

LOOK! A SPEAR-BEARER!

AH!

WHAT A **FINE** THROWING STICK!

THOSE STRANGE SPIRITS WHO ENTERED THE MOUNTAIN EARLIER THIS NIGHT...

PERHAPS IT IS FROM **THEM!**

WHHOK!

51

YOU GIVE THEM *WEAPONS*?!

AMONG OTHER THINGS...

AND YOU NEVER WORRY THAT THEY MIGHT *ATTACK* YOU ONE DAY?

ATTACK US?!

THEY *WORSHIP* US, WOLF-RIDER!

HOLD ON!

BLUE MOUNTAIN DWINDLES IN THE DISTANCE --

--AND THE LAND "SPREADS OUT LIKE A MANY-COLORED CLOAK FAR BELOW."

SKYWISE IS OBLIVIOUS TO THE PASSAGE OF TIME. HE SEES MORE IN ONE GLANCE THAN ALL HE HAS SEEN IN HIS ENTIRE LIFE.

EVENTUALLY THE ROLLING HILLS END AT THE SHORES OF AN UNBELIEVABLY HUGE BODY OF WATER.

ON AND ON IT RIPPLES -- BUT THE OPPOSITE SHORE REMAINS EVER BEYOND VIEW.

FOR ONCE, SKYWISE'S WIT FAILS HIM. HE IS STRUCK DUMB WITH AWE.

WE CALL THIS THE *VASTDEEP* WATER.

IT BEGINS HERE, BUT I DON'T THINK IT EVER ENDS.

THE GREAT BIRD CIRCLES.

THE GRAY SEA SPARKLES--

--AS DO THE STARS FLOATING IN A GRAY "VASTDEEP" OF THEIR OWN.

THEY ARE NO CLOSER--

--BUT THEY ARE THE SAME FRIENDLY COMPANIONS WHO SHONE OVER THE HOLT--

--IN THE DESERT SKY-- AND WHO NOW SHINE HIGH ABOVE THE GLIDERS' MOUNTAIN DOMAIN.

UNDER THE STARS, ALL LANDS ARE ONE--

--BUT NO LESS WONDROUS.

WELL..?

WOULD YOU... LET ME BE ALONE..?

JUST FOR A WHILE... PLEASE.

LATER, AS THE WOLF-RIDERS' COUNCIL RESUMES...

WHAT *I* DON'T LIKE IS THERE'S NO WAY OUT OF HERE EXCEPT ON THE BACKS OF THOSE BIG BIRDS!

AYE! I'LL COME AND GO AS I PLEASE OR I'LL *QUIT* THIS MOUNTAIN FOR GOOD!

BUT IF THE GLIDERS *ARE* THE *HIGH ONES*, THEY'LL LOOK AFTER OUR WANTS. *LORD VOLL* IS LIKE A FATHER-- AND HE'S ASKED US TO STAY.

HIGH ONES OR NOT, WHO SAYS WE HAVE TO LIVE WITH THEM? NO FEATHER-FACED *BIRD RIDER'S* GOING TO DO MY HUNTING FOR *ME!*

VOLL CAN JUST *WHISTLE* FOR ME IN THE WOODS!

NOW, NOW..! ONLY *WINNOWILL* HAS TRIED TO HURT ANY OF US. MOST OF THE GLIDERS ARE HARMLESS.

HUNH! YOU WOULDN'T SAY THAT IF YOU'D FOUGHT WITH US AGAINST THE *CHOSEN EIGHT.*

I WAS TIED HAND AND FOOT THEN AND YOU KNOW IT! MY POINT IS THE GLIDERS CAN NEVER MAKE US THEIR SLAVES AGAIN!

RIGHT! THEY KNOW WE'RE ON OUR GUARD NOW, THEY'VE SEEN THAT WE'RE BETTER FIGHTERS THAN THEY ARE--

--AND *LEETAH* CAN BLOCK *WINNOWILL'S* POWERS EASILY!

EASILY?! YOU TRY IT, MY FRIEND!

ENOUGH!

I'VE LISTENED TO ALL OF YOU--

--NOW YOU HEAR *ME!* HUMANS BURNED OUR HOLT, AND WE'RE *STILL* THE WOLFRIDERS.

WE LIVED WITH *LEETAH'S* FOLK FOR SEVEN TURNS OF THE SEASONS, AND WE'RE *STILL* THE WOLFRIDERS.

SOME OF YOU STAYED IN SORROW'S END, THE REST OF YOU CAME HERE TO FIND *SKYWISE* AND ME -- BUT WE'RE ALL *STILL WOLFRIDERS, WE ALWAYS WILL BE.*

I KNOW MOST OF YOU DIDN'T BELIEVE I'D FIND OTHER ELVES WHEN I SET OUT ON MY QUEST...

AND I NEVER EXPECTED TO FIND *ANYONE* LIKE THE *GLIDERS!*

BUT THEY'RE HERE, AND *WE'RE* HERE, NOW, AND FOR *DEWSHINE'S* SAKE WE MUST TRY TO GET ALONG WITH THEM... EVEN *WINNOWILL!*

WE CAN TAKE CARE OF OURSELVES -- WE ALWAYS HAVE. SO WHY SHOULD WE FEAR THE GLIDERS? THEY CAN'T CHANGE US.

NOTHING CAN DO THAT!

"NOTHING?" WHAT ABOUT *YOU, CUTTER,* BLOOD OF TEN CHIEFS? YOU LOOK LIKE ONE OF *THEM* NOW, AND YOU THINK AS NO WOLFRIDER CHIEFTAIN EVER THOUGHT BEFORE!

IF ANYTHING CHANGES US IT WILL BE *YOU* --

-- BECAUSE YOU'RE CHIEF AND WE MUST FOLLOW YOU!!

55

AT ONCE SKYWISE, NIGHTFALL AND REDLANCE RISE TO STAND WITH CUTTER.

WE FOLLOW--

--BECAUSE WE CHOOSE TO!

WHAT DOES THAT PROVE? YOU DO IT FOR LOVE!

SO WHAT? CUTTER'S MADE A LOT OF GUESSES ON THIS QUEST--

--ABOUT OTHER ELVES AND HUMANS AND HOW TO DEAL WITH THEM.

BUT HE'S BEEN RIGHT SO FAR!

I TRUST HIS HUNCHES A LOT MORE THAN YOUR STUBBORNESS!

IF YOU'RE NOT CURIOUS ABOUT THE WORLD, I AM! MORE THAN EVER!

THERE'S MORE TO LIFE THAN HUNTING AND HOWLING! NOW GO ON-- TELL ME I'M NOT A WOLFRIDER!

MMM!

BUT WHAT ABOUT SAVAH'S MESSAGE--

--THE EVIL HER SPIRIT SENSED IN YOUR PATH?

SUNTOP SAYS IT'S HERE!

SAVAH'S NOT A FIGHTER!

SHE HAS FEARS WE DON'T NEED TO HAVE.

THEN WE BROUGHT YOU HER WARNING FOR NOTHING!

JUST THEN BRIERSTING'S EARS PRICK UP--

--HIS NOSTRILS TWITCH AND HIS TAIL WAGS FRANTICALLY.

THE WOLFRIDERS LISTEN. FAINTLY, THROUGH LAYERS AND LAYERS OF ROCK COMES A THIN THREAD OF SOUND...

IT IS THE CALL OF THEIR WOLF-FRIENDS HOWLING IN THE TWILIGHT BEFORE DAWN.

FOR THREE NIGHTS THE WOLVES HAVE WAITED PATIENTLY FOR THEIR ELFIN RIDERS, WHO REMAIN HIDDEN IN THE MOUNTAIN.

OOOOWWOOOOOOOO

AMONG THE HOAN G'TAY SHO, MEMBERS OF THE NIGHTWATCH SHIVER IN SPITE OF THEMSELVES.

THOUGH THEY KNOW THE WOLVES TO BE THE NEWCOMER SPIRITS' BOND BEASTS— AND THEREFORE NOT EVIL—

—THE PLAINTIVE HOWLS ARE STILL BONE-CHILLING, CALLING FORTH PRIMAL FEARS.

WAIT! THAT SOUNDS LIKE—

OWWOOOOOO

YAP YAP!

YES...I'M SURE OF IT NOW!

CHOP-LICKER HUSH!

STARJUMPER! MY WOLF FRIEND!

HE'S REJOINED THE PACK!

THAT MEANS—

—NIGHT-RUNNER...

57

...DOESN'T NEED LOOKING AFTER ANY MORE...

SOB

MANY OF THE WOLFRIDERS HAVE EXPERIENCED SUCH A LOSS. AND THOSE WHO HAVE NOT KNOW THAT ONE DAY THEY, TOO, MUST FACE THE DEATH OF THEIR FIRST WOLF-FRIEND.

FORGETTING ALL ELSE, THE TRIBE UNITES IN A LONG, MOURNFUL HOWL.

IT IS A REAFFIRMATION OF WHO THEY ARE...

BUT, MORE, IT IS A **TRIBUTE** TO A **VALIANT** OLD FRIEND WHO ONCE LED THE PACK.

THE HOWL IS FOR NIGHTRUNNER.

58

59

STRONGBOW SENDS SO THAT ONLY *CUTTER* CAN RECEIVE HIS THOUGHTS.

I CHALLENGED YOU ONCE AND LOST... BUT NOT *THIS TIME!*

YOU'RE TOO YOUNG--

--TOO FULL OF STRANGE NOTIONS!

SOMEONE HAS TO KEEP "THE WAY" ALIVE!

I'M GOING BACK TO THE WOLVES!

THE PAIN IS LIKE AN ARROW IN THE BACK.

GO, THEN! IT'S YOUR CHOICE!

SILENCE...

THE ARCHER SENDS AGAIN --THIS TIME A DESPERATE QUESTION.

"MOONSHADE, ARE YOU WITH THEM OR WITH ME..?"

WORDLESSLY THE WOLFRIDERS TROOP TOWARD "DOOR."

60

PLEASE DON'T GO!

YOU CAN'T GET OUT THIS WAY ANYWAY!

DOOR ONLY RESPONDS TO WINNOWILL!

AT THE MERE MENTION OF THAT HATED NAME, STRONGBOW'S LIP CURLS IN A SNARL!

HE BEGINS TO SEND, WITH GREATER FEROCITY THAN EVER BEFORE!

THE STRENGTH WHICH SUSTAINED HIM, KEPT HIM SILENT THROUGH WINNOWILL'S CRUELEST ASSAULT--

--IS NOW FOCUSED UPON DOOR.

RELENTLESSLY STRONGBOW FORCES HIS WILL ON THE STATUESQUE MAIDEN WHO, AFTER A LIFETIME OF PERFORMING HER FUNCTION, HAS ALL BUT BECOME STONE HERSELF.

DOOR-OPEN!

DOOR-OPEN!

DOOR-OPEN!

AND...

WHA--?

A COMMAND TO DOOR? AND SO ENRAGED! I'VE NEVER SENSED ITS LIKE!

WINNOWILL RUSHES FROM VOLL'S THRONE CHAMBER, EAGER TO SEE HER SUSPICIONS CONFIRMED.

BUT DEWSHINE, CURIOUS ABOUT THE COUNCIL'S PROGRESS, HAS ALREADY ARRIVED ON THE SCENE.

WH-WHAT'S HAPPENING?

STRONGBOW ...HE LOOKS SO STRANGE!

HE'S SENDING! I CAN ALMOST FEEL IT...HEAVY...LIKE THE AIR JUST BEFORE A SKYFIRE STORM!

61

OF COURSE... THE ARCHER!

HIS GIFTS WOULD BE WORTHY OF THE *HIGH ONES* WERE THEY NOT GOVERNED BY HIS *ANIMAL* SIDE!

NO ONE HOLDS ME!

DOOR— OPEN!!

AT LAST FAINT COMPREHENSION FLICKERS IN THE ROCK-SHAPER'S EYES.

THOUGH IT COMES FROM A TOTALLY UNFAMILIAR SOURCE, DOOR RESPONDS TO THE MENTAL COMMAND. STRONGBOW HAS WON!

CAN'T YOU *STOP* THEM, BELOVED?

HOW? WITH MY *FISTS?*

I CAN'T *FORCE* THEM TO UNDER-STAND!

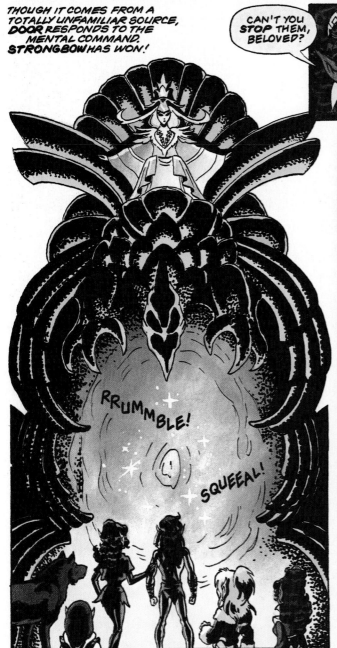

RRUMMBLE!

SQUEEAL!

STRONGBOW!

MOONSHADE!

YOU— YOU'LL NEED THESE.

YOU'LL CHANGE YOUR MINDS... I *KNOW* IT! YOU'LL COME BACK TO THE WOLVES!

COME BACK! WE'LL WAIT FOR YOU BE- LOW IN THE WOODS...

WE'LL WAIT!

GOOD, ARCHER, *GOOD!* YOU DO MY WORK FOR ME! YOUR TRIBE WILL NOT REMAIN HERE LONG IF THEY LOSE FAITH IN THEIR CHIEF.

VOLL IS DANGEROUSLY ENCHANTED WITH THE YOUTH AND VIGOR OF THE WOLFRIDERS... HE WANTS TO KEEP THEM ALWAYS UNDER HIS WING.

I CAN'T BELIEVE IT!

THEY'RE REALLY *LEAVING!*

BUT I WILL NOT PERMIT THE SAVAGES TO USURP MY POWER... HERE, I AM MISTRESS OF ALL CURIOSITY, ALL FANCY, ALL PLEASURE.

NO ONE MAY DREAM HERE, EXCEPT BY MY WHIM! NOT EVEN *LORD VOLL!*

I SHALL BE *GLAD* TO SEE THE WOLF- RIDERS GO!

NOW— ONLY ONE SMALL TASK . . . . .

63

--YOU REALIZE THAT EVEN IF YOU DO DESTROY IT, THE WOLFRIDERS MAY YET SPEAK OF IT TO *VOLL*.

WHAT GOOD IS THEIR WORD WITHOUT EVIDENCE?

TRULY, FRIEND, THERE IS ONLY *ONE* WAY TO INSURE THAT *VOLL* NEVER SEES THE PRESERVER!

IT *IS* A PITY, BUT IT MUST BE DONE!

THE NAME OF SORROW'S END NOW HOLDS A NOTE OF IRONY, FOR THE DESERT VILLAGE IS DARKENED BY THE SHADOW OF DESPAIR. *SAVAH*, THE MOTHER OF MEMORY, HAS NOT STIRRED SINCE THE GRIEVING SUN FOLK BORE HER TO HER HUT'S LOWER CHAMBER — MANY DAYS AGO.

HER BODY HAS GROWN AS FRAIL AS A WITHERED FLOWER!

OH, *SUN TOUCHER*, WHERE HAS HER SPIRIT FLOWN? WHY IS SHE UNABLE TO RETURN TO US?

ONLY *SUNTOP* MIGHT TELL US, *AHDRI*. BUT HE IS FAR AWAY—

--HOPEFULLY AT HIS FATHER'S SIDE.

YES... I, TOO, HOPE *LEETAH* AND THE WOLFRIDERS HAVE FOUND *CUTTER* AND HAVE GIVEN HIM *SAVAH'S* WARNING.

IT-IT COST HER SO *MUCH*...!

I CANNOT RID MYSELF OF THE FEELING THAT HER SPIRIT IS BEING — HELD.

"HELD," *SUN TOUCHER*? HOW? WHY?

I DO NOT KNOW.

SAVAH WARNED OF AN "EVIL!" THE PITY IS, SHE CANNOT TELL US WHAT SHAPE IT HAS — OR HOW IT HAS TOUCHED *HER*.

65

OUTSIDE, *DART* INSTRUCTS VILLAGERS IN THE USE OF THE ARROW WHIR.

LIPS GRIMLY COMPRESSED, THEY LISTEN AND LEARN WITHOUT PLEASURE.

BELOVED... I HAVE NOT ALLOWED MYSELF TO THINK IT UNTIL NOW, BUT...

DO NOT THINK IT YET, TOORAH.

THE MOTHER OF MEMORY IS THE HEART AND SOUL OF SORROW'S END. SHE *CANNOT DIE!*

REMEMBER, DON'T TWIST FORWARD WHEN YOU SHOOT.

KEEP YOUR WHIP HAND SIDE FACING THE TARGET AND SHOOT STRAIGHT OVER YOUR HEAD.

HALEK! YOUR ARM'S TOO STIFF!

THAT'S BETTER. READY..?

WHUNK! THOKK! THUNK!

MORE HITS THAN MISSES, *SUN TOUCHER.* YOUR FOLK HAVE LEARNED MUCH QUICKER THAN I EXPECTED.

MMHMM...

ANGER AND GRIEF ARE GOOD TEACHERS, *WOODLOCK.*

WITHOUT *SAVAH,* OUR ONLY SOLACE LIES IN *ACTION.*

SUCH A HEAVY TIME HAS NEVER COME UPON US. LET US HOPE *YOUR* FOLK, WHEREVER THEY ARE, HAVE FARED BETTER THAN WE.

WOODLOCK'S THOUGHTS HAVE OFTEN BEEN WITH HIS WANDERING TRIBE. THOUGH HIS CHOSEN HOME IS SORROW'S END, HE CANNOT FORGET THE HOLT, "THE WAY", OR—

WHAT?! YOU SEND BETWEEN YOURSELVES AND DISREGARD ME?! I'LL NOT TOLERATE IT!

YOU MAY WISH TO DECEIVE ME, BUT YOU KNOW YOU CANNOT MEET MY EYES —AND LIE!

FACE ME, WINNOWILL!

••••••••

I KNOW IT...TOO WELL...MY LORD.

I WAS ABOUT TO INFORM YOU THAT THE WOLF-RIDERS' COUNCIL IS DONE AND—

—ALL IS NOT WELL WITH THEM!

YOUR INVITATION TO STAY HAS CAUSED CUTTER TO LOSE TWO OF HIS FOLLOWERS.

UNFORTUNATE!

I ONLY WISHED—

—TO OFFER THE WOLF-RIDERS MY FRIENDSHIP—

"—AND TO BE NEAR THEIR CHILDREN."

DON'T BE SAD, FATHER!

AYE! LET STRONGBOW AND MOONSHADE COOL OFF IN THE WOODS A WHILE! THEY'LL BE ALL RIGHT—

—AND SO WILL WE—

—SOON AS I GET MY AXE BACK!

AND MY SPEAR!

I'M STILL CHIEF. MY FRIENDS ARE WITH ME.

MY PATH IS THEIRS NOW.

BUT CAN WE UNITE WITH THE GLIDERS AS WE DID WITH THE SUN FOLK?

WHAT WILL BECOME OF DEWSHINE—AND THE QUEST—IF WE CAN'T.

SUDDENLY A PROFOUND AND PATERNAL SENDING ENFOLDS *CUTTER* AND HIS BAND.

I GRIEVE THAT I HAVE CAUSED STRIFE AMONG YOU, WOLFRIDERS. YOU ARE MORE A *FAMILY* THAN A TRIBE. IT HAS TAKEN MUCH, I KNOW, TO DIVIDE YOU.

WINNOWILL ADVISES THAT IT WOULD BE KINDEST TO FORGET MY OWN WISHES AND TO URGE YOUR RETURN TO THE WORLD OUTSIDE.

NO! WE'RE STAYING, *LORD VOLL,* FOR MORE ANSWERS — AND FOR THE SAKE OF ONE OF OUR OWN --

"--WHO MAY SOON *BECOME* ONE OF YOURS!"

THE GLIDERS HAVE SO MANY FLY-THROUGH PLACES.

THEY'VE RIDDLED THIS MOUNTAIN--

--LIKE *WOOD WORMS* IN A ROTTEN TREE!

BUT ANY-WHERE THEY CAN FLY, I CAN CLIMB!

TYLDAK IS AFTER ME...HE KNOWS WHAT I'M UP TO...

AND NOW I-I CAN'T EVEN ASK THE *HIGH ONES* TO HELP ME GET TO *PETALWING* FIRST!

HUNTRESS THAT SHE IS, DEWSHINE QUICKLY FINDS A WAY TO TYLDAK'S CHAMBERS.

EEEEEE!! SUNNYGOLD HIGHTHING!

COME LET *PETALWING* OUT, NICE?!

HURRY! HURRY! HURRY!

69

HUSH, LITTLE ONE—

"-- OR YOU WILL BRING *TYLDAK* ON US ALL THE SOONER!'"

NEED SOMETHING HEAVY TO BREAK THE CAGE...

≡GASP≡ I HEAR *WINGS!*

FLAP
FLAP
FLAP

QUICK! WHAT CAN I USE?

THAT THING... GLEAMING LIKE METAL!

WHOOSH!

GOOD! IT'S HEAVY AND—

OOOOHH...
IT'S *HIM!*
IT'S A SYMBOL OF *TYLDAK* BEFORE HE--

NO!

SMASH!

HEE HEE HEE! *PETALWING* STRONG! *PETALWING* HAPPY!

SPOOSH!

BAD FLYHIGH~ THING *NEVER* CATCH *PETAL-WING* NOW!

≈SPUTTER≈

SOK!

LITTLE FOOL! WHAT HAVE YOU DONE?

SHE MAKES NO SOUND--

--BUT HER EYES PIERCE HIM TO THE DEEPEST PART OF HIS SOUL.

THOUGH HE RESISTS, SHE INVADES HIS ENTIRE BEING.

HE KNOWS HER...KNOWS THAT STRANGE SOUND WHICH IS HER *SOUL NAME*...

IT CRIES WITHIN HIM--

--LIKE A FLUTTERING, CAGED BIRD.

LREE....LREE....LREE...

LREE..!

I...CANNOT HURT YOU!

I *CAN!*

MOVE AWAY, TYLDAK! SHE MUST BE *PUNISHED!*

NO! I - I MEAN... THAT WOULD WASTE TIME! WE MUST FIND THE PRESERVER BEFORE *LORD VOLL*--

--YES! YOU ARE RIGHT, OF COURSE.

71

MEANWHILE...

I'VE *NEVER* TASTED FISH LIKE THIS! WHAT *FLAVORS!*

IT'S *RAW.* THAT'S ALL *I* CARE ABOUT! =URP=

TRY *CHEWING* INSTEAD OF INHALING! YOU'RE MISSING A *TREAT!*

MMMMM! NOT *DREAMBERRY* JUICE, BUT ALMOST AS GOOD!

HOW YOU *STARE* AT ME, CHILD!

DO I STILL REMIND YOU OF A "FUNNY OLD BIRD?"

ARE YOU A *HIGH ONE?*

WINNOWILL SAYS YOU ARE, BUT I DON'T LIKE *HER!*

EMBER...! SHHH!

LET HER ASK!

YOU BETTER TELL THE *TRUTH!*

ARE YOU A *HIGH ONE?*

WINNOWILL HAS MANY SECRETS, CHILD. BUT SHE NEVER SPEAKS LIES... IN *MY* PRESENCE.

SILENCE DESCENDS ON THE DINING CHAMBER AS THE WOLFRIDERS WEIGH THE IMPLICATIONS OF *LORD VOLL'S* WORDS.

FINALLY *TREESTUMP* RISES.

AHEM!

OUR LEGENDS SAY THE *HIGH ONES* FELL FROM THE HEART OF A SKY-FIRE STORM.

THEY CAME TO THIS WORLD INSIDE A "*MOUNTAIN THING*" AND WERE DRIVEN FROM IT BY HUMANS.

TRUE...

YES..! YOUR LEGENDS ARE...*TRUE!*

"MOUNTAIN THING...?"

BLUE MOUNTAIN?!

AS THOUGH STRAINING TO SEE THROUGH A HEAVY MIST, *VOLL* IS UNAWARE OF HIS EAGER QUESTIONERS. HE SPEAKS HALTINGLY, WITH A VOICE THAT WAS YOUNG WHEN LEGENDS WERE LIVED AS REALITY.

THERE... WAS A STORM...

THOSE FIRSTCOMERS... THOSE WHO GAVE ME LIFE... WERE FORCED TO WANDER LONG AND FAR IN THIS HOSTILE WORLD. ...THEN *I* WAS BORN.

THE YOUNG OF MY GENERATION... THE NEXT... AND THE NEXT... ALWAYS TURNED TO *ME* FOR GUIDANCE.... *ALWAYS!* WHY, THEN, DID THEY REBEL AGAINST MY WISDOM? WHY DID SO FEW, AT LAST, HEED MY WARNING?

"I SAW HOW THIS WORLD WOULD CHANGE THE CHILDREN OF THE *HIGH ONES* — MY CHILDREN — DIMINISH THEM IN SIZE AND POWER, MAKE THEM FORGET THE GLORY OF THE FIRSTCOMERS AND THEIR WAYS."

"BLUE MOUNTAIN IS A *HAVEN* FOR THOSE WHO REFUSED TO BE CHANGED."

74

I LED THEM HERE, WHERE WE COULD SHUT OUT THE PITILESS WORLD AND ITS INFLUENCES *FOREVER!*

THOUGH HARD-SHIP DEVOURED MY PARENTS... THEY LIVE ON IN *US*.

LORD VOLL ...BEFORE YOU CAME TO BLUE MOUNTAIN, WHERE DID YOU DWELL?

WHERE..?

YOU ASK ME TO REMEMBER ...THE *OUTSIDE?*

PLEASE! WAS IT A *GREEN GROWING PLACE?*

GREEN... GREEN LEAVES AND LIMBS... AND TWINING VINES...

YES..! OUR NUMBERS ONCE POPULATED THE WOODS--

WE WERE FLOATERS AND FIRE MAKERS...TREE SHAPERS...ROCK SHAPERS...

PSST! *NONNA* AND *ADAR'S* CAVE-HUT..:?!

UH HUH! THAT EXPLAINS THE TRACES OF ROCK-SHAPER MAGIC WE FOUND THERE!

BUT TELL ME, *CUTTER*-- YOU WHO ARE OF THE OUTSIDE BY CHOICE-- WHAT OF *YOUR* TRIBE?

IT IS ONE THING TO BOND WITH HUNTING BIRDS AS THE *CHOSEN EIGHT,* OF NECESSITY, MUST DO.

BUT I SENSE DEEPER LOYALTIES BETWEEN YOUR WOLVES AND THEIR RIDERS.

HOW DID THE WOLFRIDERS BEGIN?

CUTTER DRAWS HIM-SELF UP PROUDLY--

--READY TO RECOUNT IN LUSTY DETAIL THE COLORFUL HISTORY OF HIS TRIBE.

BUT--

LEETAH! WHA--?

OOPS!

SPLASH!

AWWW..! HERE! DRY OFF WITH THIS!

WOOPS!

BUMP!

FLASH!

"KLINK!

YAAH!

HE'S ON FIRE!!

HEY!

THE SHIRT! GET IT OFF HIM!!

I'LL SET YOUR RUMP ON FIRE, SQUIRREL CHEEKS! TAKE A WALK AND DRY YOURSELF OUT!

OOF!

BOOT!

⸮HIC⸮ ⸮GIGGLE⸮ SORRY! C'MON, SCOUTER, CHEER UP!

WHEN I'VE LIVED AS LONG AS YOU HAVE, LORD VOLL, MAYBE THEN I'LL GET MORE RESPECT!

BE GLAD THAT YOU ARE LOVED AS WELL AS RESPECTED, YOUNG CHIEF,

AS ARE YOU, VOLL, LORD OF THE GLIDERS!

WHILE CUTTER GRUMBLINGLY GOES TO RETRIEVE HIS FUR VEST, ARODEE GUIDES SCOUTER, PIKE AND SKYWISE THROUGH MAZE-LIKE CORRIDORS.

SO THE CHOSEN EIGHT AND *TYLDAK* ARE THE ONLY GLIDERS WHO EVER GO OUTSIDE?

THE CHOSEN EIGHT ARE *LORD VOLL'S* HUNTERS.

THROUGH US HE PROVIDES FOR ALL THOSE WHO DWELL INSIDE THE MOUNTAIN.

BUT *ARODEE,* DOESN'T IT DRIVE YOU *MAD* LIVING HERE? YOU COULD ESCAPE *EASILY!*

THE WORLD IS SO *BIG!* JUST WAITING TO BE EXPLORED! HAVEN'T YOU EVER BEEN TEMPTED TO FLY AWAY AND JUST KEEP FLYING?

≶CHUCKLE≷

WHAT NONSENSE! *NOTHING* CAN COMPARE WITH THE WONDERS WE'VE MADE HERE!

LOOK AROUND YOU! LOOK AND SEE WHAT THE *HIGH ONES* CAN DO!

EVERYTHING WE TOUCH IS BETTER AND MORE BEAUTIFUL FOR HAVING BEEN SHAPED BY OUR WILLS.

WHAT SHOULD WE SEEK OUTSIDE WHEN ALL THE WORLD IS HERE?

WHAT ABOUT *FUN?*

WHAT ABOUT THINGS TO DO?

WE DO THINGS--

--IN WAYS *YOU* CAN SCARCELY IMAGINE!

COME... I'LL SHOW YOU!

78

...THREE...FOUR...FIVE...LOOKS LIKE **SIX**. SIX EGGS, ONE INSIDE THE OTHER!

BUT WHAT USE IS IT TO SHAPE FANCY SYMBOLS ON THE INNERMOST EGG?

I CAN'T SEE THEM.

YOU CAN--

--BUT YOU MUST BE WILLING TO LOSE YOURSELF ENTIRELY IN CONTEMPLATION. ALL THE SECRETS OF EXISTENCE ARE HIDDEN IN THOSE SYMBOLS. AND SINCE LIFE IS ENDLESS FOR ELVES, *EGG'S* WORK IS ALSO ENDLESS, EVER GROWING...SPINNING...

EACH NEWLY FORMED SYMBOL CHANGES THE MEANING OF ALL THE OTHERS.

FOREVER IS NOT TIME ENOUGH TO UNDERSTAND SUCH A WORK --EVEN FOR THE **HIGH ONES**.

WINNOWILL SERVES HIM A POTION NOW AND THEN -- THE SAME DRINK SHE GIVES TO *BRACE* AND *DOOR*.

IT IS ALL THEY SEEM TO NEED.

HUNH! DOES HE *EAT*?

SOUR FACE! BET HE HASN'T CRACKED A SMILE SINCE *TREESTUMP* WAS A CUB!

HMM...

AROREE...YOU GLIDERS SAY YOU'RE THE *HIGH ONES*, AND...WELL...*LORD VOLL* IS SO OLD I GUESS HE HAS THE RIGHT TO BELIEVE ANYTHING HE WANTS.

BLUE MOUNTAIN IS A WORLD ALL ITS OWN -- AND IT'S *FANTASTIC*!

BUT EGG, BRACE AND DOOR...

THEY--THEY'VE *BECOME* WHAT THEY DO!

THEY'RE NOT *LIVING*!

I DON'T KNOW HOW TO SAY IT, BUT--

--IT'S *WRONG*!

SKYWISE... *YOU* ARE ALIVE! YOU MAKE ME FEEL--

≷GASP≷ WHAT'S *HAPPENING*!?

HUH?

PIKE! WHAT DID YOU *DO?!*

UH... I--

--I JUST THOUGHT OLD *EGG* NEEDED CHEERING UP!

GAVE HIM A SIP!

:TSK TSK: GOT NO *TOLERANCE* I GUESS!

UH OH...

WINNOWILL! SHE'LL BE *FURIOUS* ABOUT *EGG!*

ANYONE WANT TO TRY *APOLOGIZING* TO HER?

"NOOOO..!"

RIGHT!

MOMENTS LATER...

HEH HEH HEH DID YOU SEE HER *SCOWL?* DARK AS A *STORM CLOUD!*

THANKS TO *YOU,* YOU *WINE SACK!*

80

DEWSHINE!

SOB

SCOUTER..! LOVEMATE...

I-I'M SO SORRY... SO SORRY THAT--

HUSH!

ARE YOU --ALL RIGHT?

NEVER MIND ABOUT ME! YOU MUST HELP ME SAVE LITTLE *PETALWING!*

PETAL-WHO?

PETALWING!

I HATE TO ADMIT IT, BUT I'VE *MISSED* THAT SCREECHING BUG!

WHERE IS IT, ANYWAY?

YOU - YOU *KNOW* ABOUT --?

LAUGHING, SKYWISE RELATES THE TALE OF THE FORBIDDEN GROVE --

--AND HOW THE COLORFUL, WINGED SPRITE ATTACHED ITSELF TO LEETAH.

BUT HIS SMILE FADES --

--AS DEWSHINE TELLS OF WINNOWILL'S DEADLY PLANS FOR PETALWING.

YOU KNOW... I THINK IT'S TIME WE PUT THAT SHE-SNAKE IN HER PLACE!

AND I KNOW JUST WHO CAN DO IT BEST!

SHORTLY...

THERE... I HAVE CLEANSED YOU— AND NOW YOU CAN RESTORE THE GREAT EGG.

I SWEAR NO ONE SHALL TAMPER WITH YOU AGAIN!

WINNOWILL...

I MUST HAVE WORDS WITH YOU.

WORDS! I'LL NOT WASTE WORDS ON YOU!

LOOK WHAT YOUR FRIENDS HAVE DONE!

STUPID, UNRULY SAVAGES!

S-STOP!

YOUR ANGER..!

I-I CANNOT--

VERY WELL. SINCE YOU ARE SO INEPT AT SENDING, I SHALL SPEAK PLAINLY.

YOU AND THE WOLF-RIDERS ARE TO LEAVE BLUE MOUNTAIN, NOW—AND FOREVER!

YOU FEAR US! I HAVE SENSED IT ALL ALONG!

SINCE WE CAME HERE YOU'VE DONE NOTHING BUT HINT, BEHIND A SLY SMILE, THAT YOU DO NOT WANT US TO STAY!

WHY?

?

LEETAH?

I CANNOT BELIEVE THAT A TRUE HIGH ONE WOULD BE SO COLD AND UNLOVING.

TIMMORN'S BLOOD!

SHE'S ALONE —WITH WINNOWILL!

AND WHY DO YOU WANT TO HARM PETALWING?

DO NOT SPEAK! I *KNOW* THE TRUTH AND I WILL KEEP IT TO MYSELF — IF YOU AND THE WOLFRIDERS LEAVE—

—*NOW.*

COME NOW... I, TOO, AM A HEALER.

YOU KNOW *NOTHING!!*

I TOUCHED *STRONG-BOW*...AND I *LEARNED*... JUST AS *YOU* SURELY LEARNED, THE FIRST TIME YOU TOUCHED A WOLFRIDER.

TELL ME, DARK SISTER...

HOW DID YOU RECONCILE YOURSELF—

—TO THE *TAINT* IN *CUTTER'S* BLOOD?

GO ON... YOU CAN SPEAK FREELY TO *ME*..!

DID IT *THRILL* YOU—

—THE MINGLING OF HIS BLOOD WITH YOURS?

IT *IS* EXCITING TO FLIRT WITH *DEATH*... IS IT NOT?

STOP!

THE WOLFRIDERS ARE, INDEED, BROTHERS TO THEIR SHORT-LIVED WOLVES. I WONDER HOW THEY BECAME SO, AND WHEN?

LONG AGO, I SHOULD THINK...

OR DO THEY CONTINUE TO RENEW THEIR BLOOD KIN-SHIP EVEN NOW?

BE SILENT!

CUTTER SPOKE OF LIVING AS LONG AS *LORD VOLL.*

HOW PATHETIC!

OBVIOUSLY THE WOLFRIDERS ARE IGNORANT OF THE *PRICE* THEY MUST EVENTUALLY PAY FOR THEIR ANCESTORS' FOLLY!

84

LET THEM *CONTINUE* IN THEIR INNOCENCE! I WILL NOT TELL THEM, AND *YOU* WILL NOT!

HOW COULD I...?

IF THEY WERE *GONE* FROM BLUE MOUNTAIN?

Y-YOU'VE WON.

I WILL TRY TO CONVINCE *CUTTER* TO LEAVE.

NO, LEETAH!

WINNOWILL'S USED TO SPYING, ...NOT TO BEING SPIED ON!

SHE HAS NO HOLD OVER YOU—*NOW!*

≋CHOKE≋

I HAVE THE BLOOD OF *WOLVES* IN MY VEINS—IT'S TRUE.

I SCENT... AND STALK—

—AND *HEAR* LIKE A WOLF!

SO... NOW YOU KNOW THAT SOMEDAY YOU MUST GROW OLD AND *DIE* LIKE A WOLF.

I KNOW YOU *LIE* WHENEVER IT SUITS YOU—

"—BUT I MUST BELIEVE *LEETAH.*"

WELL PLAYED, WOLFRIDER! MY *CARELESSNESS* HAS COST ME A *WEAPON*—THOUGH BY NO MEANS MY MOST POTENT ONE!

THINK WELL WHAT IT MAY COST *YOU* TO REMAIN HERE!

85

THE CURVED BLADE COLD AGAINST HER PALE THROAT, **WINNOWILL** BLASTS CUTTER WITH THE KIND OF PAIN ONLY SHE CAN GIVE.

HER BLACK SENDING DEALS THE HURT — HER CLAWS DIRECT AND INTENSIFY IT. SUDDEN AGONY SHOOTS THROUGH HIS LIMBS, BURSTS LIKE FLAME BEHIND HIS EYES!

YET HIS STRENGTH DOES NOT GIVE WAY!

"THE WOLFRIDERS ARE, INDEED, BROTHERS TO THEIR SHORT-LIVED WOLVES." HOW DID THEY BECOME SO? AND WHEN? LONG AGO...

LONG AGO... IN THE LAND OF THE FROZEN MOUNTAINS — A LAND GRIPPED BY CRUSHING COLD, WHERE A HANDFUL OF ICE-PALE OUTCASTS STRUGGLED TO SURVIVE. AMONG THEM THERE WAS ONE TO WHOM THE WORLD WAS NOT AN ENEMY. *TIMMAIN*, A *HIGH ONE*, A FIRSTCOMER, WHOSE MAGIC POWERS WERE STRONG.

SHE ALONE LEARNED TO FULLY TAP THE FORCES NATIVE TO THE TWO-MOONED PLANET. SHE ALONE COULD SING INTO WHOLENESS THE CRIPPLED POWERS OF HER BRETHREN.

TIMMAIN, THE SELF-SHAPER, EMBRACED NATURE'S MANY FORMS, BECAME ONE WITH THE GREAT PROVIDER FOREST, KNEW ITS SECRETS AND ITS SIGNS.

THE SEASONS TURNED IN THEIR MANY EIGHTS. *TIMMAIN* WATCHED OVER HER FOLK AND FELT THE WHITE COLD GROW DEEPER.

IT DROVE THE LIFE FROM THE FOREST UNTIL ELVES AND BEASTS OF PREY ALIKE SHARED THE SHARP PANGS OF STARVATION. HUMBLY *TIMMAIN* SOUGHT AID FROM THOSE WHO FIRST TAUGHT HER PEOPLE TO HUNT — THE WOLVES.

IF ONLY SHE MIGHT BORROW THE SHAPE AND STRENGTH OF THOSE SHAGGY PRE-DATORS, SHE COULD HELP SUPPLY HER TRIBE WITH MEAT.

IT WAS DONE. AND DONE WELL. SHE RAN WITH THE HOWLING PACK AND BURIED HER FANGS IN WARM FLESH AND BLOOD.

EVERY DAY SHE BROUGHT HER CATCHES TO HER GRATEFUL TRIBEFOLK. BUT THERE CAME A TIME WHEN DAYS WOULD PASS WITHOUT HER RETURN.

AND WHEN SHE DID APPEAR, SHE SEEMED LESS *TIMMAIN* AND MORE WOLF. THE ELF SOUL WITHIN THE BEAST BODY WAS FADING.
HER ANXIOUS FRIENDS TRIED EVERY MEANS TO SUMMON HER BACK TO HER FORMER SHAPE.

BUT TO NO AVAIL.

THE TRANSFORMATION WAS TOO COMPLETE.

THOUGH SHE NEVER TURNED ON HER TRIBE, THEY WERE NO LONGER HER BRETHREN. OFTEN THEY SAW HER RUNNING WITH THE LEADER OF THE WOLFPACK. IT WAS CLEAR WHERE HER ALLEGIANCE LAY.

FROM THE NEW BONDS *TIMMAIN* HAD FORMED AND THE NEW WAY SHE NOW FOLLOWED --

-- THERE SPRANG A NEW LIFE!

ONE WHICH PROVED THAT TIMMAIN WAS NOT YET ENTIRELY A WOLF.

SHE RAISED THE STRANGE-LOOKING CUB, FED HIM FROM HER OWN MOUTH, PROTECTED HIM FROM HARM.

YET THE DAY CAME WHEN THE REMAINING SPARK OF A HIGH ONE'S WISDOM TOLD TIMMAIN THAT THE CUB'S ELF BLOOD MUST BE ACKNOWLEDGED.

SHE BROUGHT THE YOUNGLING INTO HER FORMER TRIBEFOLK'S CARE, AND THAT NIGHT SHE DISAPPEARED, NEVER TO BE SEEN AGAIN.

THEY NAMED HIM *TIMMORN YELLOW EYES.* THEY TAUGHT HIM TO SPEAK AND TO SEND —AND TO LOVE HIS MOTHER'S KIND AS WELL AS HIS FATHER'S. FEROCIOUS AND POWERFUL, HE BECAME THE PROTECTOR OF ELVES AND WOLVES— DRAWING THE TWO TRIBAL GROUPS TOGETHER IN A FIRM AND ENDURING ALLIANCE.

91

TO THE ELVES, ALWAYS FEW IN NUMBER, MIGHTY **TIMMORN** WAS CHIEF. TO HIS SIRE, THE PACK'S LEADER, HE WAS FRIEND AND EQUAL. **TIMMORN** LED HIS KINDRED AWAY FROM THE FROZEN MOUNTAINS IN SEARCH OF NEWGREEN WOODS AND GOOD HUNTS. SO THE WOLFRIDERS BEGAN, AND SO, TOO, BEGAN THEIR EVERLASTING RIVALRY WITH HUMANS.

TIMMORN YELLOW-EYES SIRED CUBS BOTH IN AND OUTSIDE OF RECOGNITION. HE FOUGHT, AGED AND FINALLY DIED EVER PROUD OF HIS HALF-WOLF BLOOD.

THAT BLOOD CONTINUED TO FLOW THROUGH TEN GENERATIONS OF WOLFRIDER CHIEFTAINS AND THEIR TRIBEFOLK.

IT MADE THEM STRONG, SWIFT AND STURDY, EQUAL TO ANY CHALLENGE — IT TIED THEM BEYOND ALL UNTYING TO THE WORLD AND ITS CYCLE OF LIFE.

AND IF THE PRICE WAS MORTALITY, NO ONE KNEW IT — FOR RARE, INDEED, WAS THE WOLFRIDER WHO DIED PEACEFULLY OF OLD AGE!

THIS TRUTH WINNOWILL NOW KNOWS IN HER SOUL — SHE HAS MET HER MATCH IN STRENGTH BORN OF THE WORLD OUTSIDE!

NO, BELOVED! THE PAIN IS BLINDING YOU!!

REMEMBER THE BRIDGE OF DESTINY?

REMEMBER HOW YOU SAVED *RAYEK'S* LIFE? WHY DID YOU DO IT?

REMEMBER!

HIS AGONY RELIEVED BY LEETAH'S HEALING EMBRACE, CUTTER RECALLS...

NO ELF MUST DIE...

EVEN IF HE *IS* MY ENEMY!

IT IS THE HARDEST CHOICE HE HAS EVER MADE — A CHOICE BETWEEN INSTINCT AND ETHIC.

HE CHOOSES... AND *THIS* TIME HE FEELS NO TRIUMPH.

YOU ARE WISE, LEETAH.

YOU HAVE JUST SAVED HIS LIFE!

DO NOT DECEIVE YOURSELF. I SAVED *YOU!*

YOU MAY BE ABLE TO TWIST AND BEND YOUR OWN FLIMSY PEOPLE LIKE *PLAYTHINGS*—

—BUT YOU CAN *NEVER* DEFEAT A WOLFRIDER'S SPIRIT!

IT IS THE SPIRIT OF *LIFE ITSELF!*

TYLDAK FLIES AWAY, RAGING IN FRUSTRATION. WINNOWILL SLINKS TO HER OWN QUARTERS, AND ALL THAT REMAINS IS ECHOING SILENCE.

ALONE, NOW, IN THE CHAMBER OF EGG, CUTTER AND LEETAH FACE EACH OTHER--

--AND THE FUTURE.

FOR WHAT?

I KNOW WHY YOU HID THE TRUTH. I UNDERSTAND.

WE'LL KEEP IT OUR SECRET --FOR NOW.

CAN YOU FORGIVE ME... MY LIFEMATE?

BESIDES, BEARCLAW ALWAYS SAID A WOLFRIDER'S LIFE WAS SHORT.

I NEVER KNEW DIFFERENT UNTIL I MET SAVAH-- THEN I DREAMED OF LIVING FOREVER.

BUT I'M AWAKE, NOW, AND THE TRUTH IS GOOD.

I'M JUST SORRY WINNOWILL TORMENTED YOU NEEDLESSLY.

THAT IS WHY YOU MUSTN'T LET WINNOWILL DRIVE US FROM THIS MOUNTAIN!

YOUR FATHER WAS WRONG! ?SOB? YOU WILL LIVE LONG, BELOVED, AND ALL THE QUESTIONS YOU HAVE DARED TO ASK WILL BE ANSWERED!

95

"I DID NOT WANT **LORD VOLL** TO LEARN OF YOUR WOLF BLOOD FOR FEAR THAT HIS HEART WOULD HARDEN AGAINST THE WOLFRIDERS—JUST AS MINE ONCE DID."

"**VOLL** IS FIRST-BORN OF THE **HIGH ONES**—"

—HE KNOWS THINGS ABOUT OUR KIND THAT WE CAN **NEVER** LEARN ANYWHERE ELSE!

IF ONLY WE CAN MAKE HIM REMEMBER!

SO... AT LAST MY **LEETAH** BELIEVES IN THE **QUEST!**

YES, BELOVED! I HOWL FOR **YOU!**

AND COME WHAT MAY—

—WE'LL BE **TOGETHER!**

M—MISTRESS..?

98

HA HA HA HA HA HA HA HA HA HA

YOU WILL AID ME IN THIS-- --AS WILL THE TWO OTHERS I NOW SUMMON.

TYLDAK! KUREEL! MEET ME IN TENSPAN'S HALL WITH-OUT DELAY!

AT THE SAME TIME... THE WOLFRIDERS' YOUNG CHIEF STILL ACHES FROM HIS TRIUMPH OVER WINNOWILL, BUT THE HEALING HANDS OF HIS LIFEMATE, LEETAH, HAVE NOW EASED THE WORST OF THE PAIN.

I TELL YOU AGAIN --YOU MUSTN'T BE PROUD OF WHAT I DID!

BUT I AM PROUD --OF YOU!

YOU COULD HAVE KILLED WINNOWILL--

--YET YOU LET HER LIVE! SHE IS ALL THE MORE HUMBLED FOR IT!

AND YOUR HANDS--

--ARE NOT STAINED WITH THE BLOOD OF YOUR OWN KIND!

THAT'S JUST IT! I TOUCHED MINDS WITH WINNOWILL!

SHE'S AN ELF BUT NOT MY KIND AND NOT YOUR KIND! SHE THREATENED OUR CUBS!

SHE'S--

LISTEN, IF IT HADN'T BEEN FOR YOU, SHE'D BE DEAD NOW--

--AND I--I'D BE GLAD!

WOULD YOU? THEN I AM GLAD THAT YOU SPARED HER --IF ONLY FOR MY SAKE.

SURELY HER THREATS WERE MEANT ONLY TO FRIGHTEN US AWAY. SHE WOULDN'T --COULDN'T HURT SUNTOP AND EMBER!

COULD SHE..?

COME! LET'S HURRY BACK AND TELL LORD VOLL ABOUT WINNOWILL--

--ABOUT PETALWING--

--EVERYTHING!

CUTTER AND LEETAH DASH FOR THE GLIDERS' MAIN DINING CHAMBER WHERE SUNTOP, EMBER AND THE WOLFRIDERS BASK IN LORD VOLL'S ATTENTION.

99

BUT BEFORE THE ANXIOUS PARENTS CAN REACH THEIR DESTINATION...

LEETAH! CUTTER! WAIT!

IT'S DEWSHINE!

TIMMORN'S BLOOD! SHE'S SICK! LITTLE COUSIN, WHAT'S *WRONG?*

OH, *CUTTER!* EVERYTHING YOU SAID ABOUT RECOGNITION IS *TRUE!* IT'S *TERRIBLE!*

ONLY IF YOU RESIST IT, *DEWSHINE!*

I KNOW... I *KNOW!*

BUT YOU *DID* FIGHT IT, LEETAH! TELL ME HOW! I-I DON'T *WANT* THIS! I WANT TO BE A WOLF-RIDER! *ALWAYS!*

THAT UGLY TYLDAK CAN'T TAKE YOU AWAY FROM US--

--EVEN IF YOU *HAVE* RECOGNIZED HIM!

YOU SEE HIS *SOUL!* IT WAS THE SAME FOR ME!

THOUGH I REJECTED *CUTTER'S* OUTWARD MANNER--

HE ISN'T *UGLY!!*

WHEN I LOOK AT HIM I SEE ...I SEE HIM AS HE WAS BEFORE *WINNOWILL* CHANGED HIM!

--I KNEW HE WAS PART OF ME,...FROM THE MOMENT OUR EYES MET.

100

COULDN'T IT BE THAT WAY WITH YOU AND *TYLDAK?*

NO!!

(SOB) HELP ME, LEETAH!

I WON'T SUBMIT TO THIS, I WON'T!

I'LL BE A WOLFRIDER AND BEAR A WOLFRIDER'S CUB--

--OR I'LL DIE!!

SHHH...I WILL HELP YOU ALL I CAN, KITLING.

RECOGNITION WAS FIRST A CURSE AND THEN A BLESSING TO ME--

I HOPE IT CAN BE SO FOR Y--! OH!

PETALWING BEEN INSIDE HIDEY-HOLE TOO LONG!

WANT TO SEE SUNNYGOLD HIGHTHING!

HELLO! HELLO!

§SNIFF§ Y-YOU'RE SAFE!

AT HIS FIRST SIGHT OF PETALWING, SCOUTER GRINS, PARTLY IN AMAZEMENT, MOSTLY IN JOY THAT DEWSHINE'S TEARS HAVE CHANGED TO SMILES.

MEANWHILE, LIKE LIVING SHADOWS, THREE CONSPIRATORS AVOID THE TORCHLIGHT WHICH SPILLS FROM ONE OF THE DINING CHAMBER'S MANY ARCHWAYS.

REMEMBER, I AM WITH YOU IN THIS ONLY SO LONG AS LORD VOLL IS NOT HARMED!

101

YOU SWEAR THAT HE WILL *SLEEP* AND NOTHING WORSE?

NOTHING WORSE, *KUREEL.* YOU KNOW MY POWERS. THE MEREST *TOUCH* OF MY MIND TO A CERTAIN PART OF HIS WILL PLUNGE HIM INTO DREAMLESS OBLIVION.

WE'VE SEEN THE SAVAGES' FIERCE ATTACHMENT TO THEIR CHILDREN. THEY WILL HUNT YOU DOWN AND *KILL YOU!*

I HAVE MY OWN MEANS OF ESCAPE. THEY WILL NOT BE ABLE TO FOLLOW ME.

KUREEL, YOU CLAIM THAT OTHERS OF THE CHOSEN EIGHT HATE THE WOLFRIDERS AS YOU DO. IT IS TIME TO USE THAT HATE TO OUR ADVANTAGE.

-- AND THE BIG BIRD *SWOOPED* DOWN AND OUR *ZWOOT* RAN AWAY WITH MOTHER HANGING UNDERNEATH AND US IN THE BASKET *(GASP)* AND IT GOT DARK AND WE GOT LOST IN THE WOODS AND WENT TO SLEEP AND ALL THE LITTLE *SPITTY BUGS* WRAPPED US UP IN GOOEY THREADS *(GASP)* AND FATHER CUT US OUT AND *PETALWING* FOLLOWED US AND IT SINGS *REAL BAD* AND--

BLABBERMOUTH!

THAT'S NO WAY TO TELL A STORY!

LORD VOLL DOESN'T BELIEVE IT!

I BELIEVE IN YOU BOTH--

--AND I CAN LISTEN TO ANY AMOUNT OF CHATTER!

YOUR VOICES ARE SO SWEET.

BUT PETAL-WING ISN'T A "SPITTY BUG!" IT TALKS AND IT LOOKS ALMOST LIKE US EXCEPT--

--EXCEPT IT'S TINY AND IT HAS PRETTY WINGS AND --

NOW!

KUREEL SENDS TO HIS COHORTS AT THE TABLE...

PIKE?

THE RESPONSE IS IMMEDIATE--

ZZZRZZ...

HEH HEH PIKE?

--AND TOTALLY UNEXPECTED!

GASP!

CHOKE

UNNH!

REDLANCE!

WHA-?

CRASH!

BACKBITING ROCK RAT!

TEACH HIM, TREESTUMP!

GLADLY!

OFF!

COUGH COUGH

AAH!

103

104

AT THE SOUND OF WINNOWILL'S CRY--

K-KRIK! KRRAK! KRRAK

K-RRUMBLE!

GLOATING, SHE STEPS ONTO THE SHATTERED SCULPTURE'S BASE--

FATHER!

--AND INSTANTLY DROPS OUT OF SIGHT!

EVEN AS HE DIVES AFTER HER--

SHE'S ESCAPING THROUGH A TUNNEL!

--CUTTER KNOWS THAT HE IS ALREADY TOO LATE.

THE ROCK, IT'S MOVING --PUSHING ME UP AGAIN!

HE CALLS TO HIS SON...

THE ONLY REPLY IS STONE SCRAPING AGAINST SWIFTLY RISING STONE.

MY CUB! SHE HAS MY CUB!

106

FURIOUS, HE RUNS BACK TO THE DINING CHAMBER...

SIX OF YOU WERE HERE—AND YOU COULDN'T SAVE HIM?!

WHERE WERE YOU, SKYWISE..? STEALING PLEASURE WITH AROREE WHEN YOU MIGHT HAVE BEEN THE ONE TO SAVE SUNTOP?

UH... WE DIDN'T... WELL, SEE... WE WERE FIGHTING AND —

—AND YOU, PIKE! TOO FULL OF WINE TO STAND UP LET ALONE FIGHT!

W-WELL WHERE'VE YOU BEEN, ANYWAY?

I JUST HAD A BRUSH WITH WINNOWILL MYSELF—AND I BEAT HER! BUT LIKE A FOOL I LET HER GO, BECAUSE I THOUGHT MY CUBS WERE SAFE WITH YOU!

NOW... BIRD ELF!

TELL ME WHERE THAT SHE SNAKE TOOK MY SON!

§UNNNH§

I...DO... NOT KNOW!

THERE ARE PLACES IN THIS MOUNTAIN KNOWN ONLY TO WINNOWILL! SHE WILL RETURN THE CHILD TO YOU WHEN YOU AND YOUR TRIBE HAVE LEFT OUR DOMAIN FOR GOOD!

NO TRADE! I WANT SUNTOP NOW!

TYLDAK..!

PLEASE TELL US HOW TO FIND HIM!

NOT EVEN IF I COULD! ALL WAS WELL UNTIL YOU SAVAGES CAME! LORD VOLL WAS WISER THAN HE KNEW TO SECLUDE HIS FOLLOWERS FROM THE CORRUPTING WORLD.

YOU ARE LESS FIT TO BE HERE, THAN WINNOWILL'S HUMAN PETS! HOW DARE YOU CLAIM TO BE ELVES?

WHAT?!

YOU, WHO WERE NOT CONTENT WITH THE FORM AND POWERS OF A HIGH ONE—

—YOU WHO WANTED NOT JUST TO FLOAT, BUT TO FLY LIKE A BIRD... YOU CAN SAY THINGS LIKE THAT TO ME?

WHAT ARE YOU, TYLDAK? YOUR BODY... YOUR WORDS ...YOUR VERY THOUGHTS ....ARE THEY YOUR OWN—

—OR WINNOWILL'S?

OUTSIDE, RAIN POURS IN SHEETS DOWN BLUE MOUNTAIN'S PRECIPITOUS FLANKS, SWELLING THE LONG RIVER.

THE WOODS ARE STILL, SAVE FOR THE STEADY PELTING OF RAINDROPS AND THE GROWLS OF FARAWAY THUNDER.

LIVING THINGS SEEK SHELTER IN BURROWS... IN THICKETS...

AND UNDER FALLEN TREES.

(SIGH) IT'S SO *QUIET* WITHOUT THE OTHERS.

I LIKE IT QUIET!

WHAT CAN THEY BE DOING RIGHT NOW..? AND WHAT OF *WINNOWILL?*

THAT'S *CUTTER'S* WORRY! HE GOT THEM INTO THAT MOUNTAIN...

WHATEVER HAPPENS TO THEM IS ON *HIS* HEAD, NOT *MINE!*

BUT HE *DID* FREE YOU FROM *WINNOWILL'S* CAGE.

AND ENDANGERED HIS OWN CUBS DOING IT!

I DIDN'T ASK HIM TO.

HE'S STILL A FOOLISH CUB HIMSELF.

HE'LL *NEVER* BE THE CHIEF *BEARCLAW* WAS.

BEARCLAW...

I REMEMBER YOUR MANY QUARRELS WITH HIM.

THERE WERE TIMES WHEN I FEARED YOU MIGHT *KILL* EACH OTHER.

BUT YOU ADORED *BEARCLAW...*

I THINK YOU *ENVIED CUTTER* HIS FATHER WHEN YOU LOST YOUR OWN!

WHAT?! ARE *YOU* AGAINST ME TOO?

I'M AN *ELDER!*

I NEED NO FATHER--

--AND NO STRIPLING CHIEF TO TELL ME WHAT A WOLFRIDER SHOULD BE!

I KNOW!

AND SO DO I!

WE HAVE CHOSEN TO KEEP TO *THE WAY* ...BUT AT WHAT COST? WE'RE ALL ALONE.

PERHAPS... PERHAPS WE WERE... *WRONG?*

108

A SUDDEN, URGENT SENDING, CLEAR AND MANY-VOICED, UNITES THE WOLFRIDERS BOTH WITHIN AND OUTSIDE BLUE MOUNTAIN.

OH, STRONGBOW...! THEY NEED US!

THEY NEED YOU!

ALL DOUBTS ARE SWIFTLY LAID ASIDE--

--TO ANSWER THE DEMANDS OF THE MOMENT.

DOOR, OPEN!

DOOR...

OPEN!!

CURSE IT! YOU KNOW I CAN FORCE YOU!

OPEN NOW!

@!!#*ə! HAD TO BREAK MY TAIL TO GET OUT--NOW I HAVE TO PUT IT IN A SLING TO GET BACK IN!

COME ON.

AND...

WELL... I'M BACK.

WAIT, LEETAH! SKYWISE SAYS YOU ARE A GREAT HEALER. YOU MUST AWAKEN LORD VOLL.

IT IS YOUR DUTY!

NO, AROREE. NOT UNTIL I HAVE MY SON BACK.

SO THERE!

--THEN HALF THE CHOSEN EIGHT STOOD BY WHILE THE REST OF THEM HELPED WINNOWILL TAKE SUNTOP.

ONE SWIFT ARROW BETWEEN THE EYES AND SHE'D NEVER HAVE LAID A HAND ON HIM.

I'M SORRY.

RIGHT OR WRONG I SHOULDN'T HAVE WALKED OUT ON YOU.

NO, YOU SHOULDN'T HAVE..!

109

AND *I* SHOULDN'T HAVE BEEN SO CURSED SURE THAT THE GLIDERS *WERE* OUR KIND — JUST BECAUSE THEY'RE ELVES!

RIGHT! LET'S GO FIND YOUR CUB!

AYE! FIND THE CUB AND THE CUB-THIEF!

BUT HOW?

WINNOWILL SANK THROUGH THE FLOOR AND THE HOLE SEALED OVER HER!

SHE CALLED OUT JUST BEFORE IT HAPPENED — A NAME — TWO-EDGE! REMEMBER IT, SKYWISE?

TWO-EDGE... SURE! PART TROLL, PART ELF! HE MADE *NEW MOON!*

HMMM... IF HE'S WINNOWILL'S ALLY —

AND IF HE CAN *HEAR* ME... MAYBE IT'LL MEAN SOMETHING TO HIM!

TWO-EDGE! TWO-EDGE! I AM CUTTER! THE MOON SWORD IS *STILL MINE*, KEY AND ALL!

KEY..?

ANSWER! ME!

HEH HEH HEH HEH HEH

WHERE IS MY SON, SWORD-MAKER? *SPEAK*, OR I'LL CUT YOUR LAUGHTER SHORT WITH YOUR OWN HANDIWORK!

CUTTER-ELF, SON OF BEARCLAW...

HE-HE KNOWS YOU!

SHH!

CUTTER-ELF, KEEN BLADE, TEMPERED WHERE THERE WAS NO SHADE...

TEMPERED IN THE DESERT FIRE...

WHAT IS IT THAT YOU DESIRE?

MY SON, YOU CRAZY HALF TROLL!

IF THERE'S ANY *HONOR* LEFT IN YOUR ELF BLOOD —

— MY ELF BLOOD..?! HA HA HA HA HA HA

THE SWORD HOLDS THE *KEY*... THE SWORD *IS* THE KEY!

AND CUTTER KINSEEKER HOLDS THE SWORD!

COME AND SEE! COME AND SEE!

110

WITH ALARMING SPEED THE STONE SINKS AGAIN, REVEALING WINNOWILL'S SECRET PASSAGEWAY.

IS IT MAGIC THAT MOVES THE ROCK?

WHO KNOWS? WHO KNOWS HOW A HALF-ELF, HALF TROLL DOES ANYYTHING!

WINNOWILL HAS A SON... A SUN... A SUNNY SON SUNTOP! COME AND SEE...

I WISH WE COULD TRUST THAT TWO-EDGE MORE.

OH, WELL...

LET'S GO!

I WILL NOT AID YOU. NEITHER WILL I TRY TO STOP YOU.

BEWARE.

WINNOWILL'S DEFENSES AGAINST UNWANTED COMPANY ARE MANY.

BUT NOW WE KNOW THAT HER "FRIENDS" CAN BE PERSUADED TO BETRAY HER!

FARE WELL...

FARE WELL...

LREE.

SHORTLY...

PETALWING REMEMBERS...!

OOOOOO! MUCKY-DARK CAVEPLACE!

MY LITTLE SUNTOP...IN THERE!

YOU-YOU DON'T THINK WINNOWILL WOULD--?

...YES.

SHE'S FINISHED NO MATTER WHAT SHE DOES!

YOU CAN'T SAVE HER THIS TIME, LEETAH ...UNDERSTAND?

111

112

SUNTOP SHIVERS, RECALLING THE BLACK, EMPTY PLACE WHERE HE RECEIVED SAVAH'S WARNING OF EVIL — THE VERY EVIL HE NOW FACES!

I HATE YOU!!

YOU'RE CRUEL!

WHY DO YOU TRY TO HURT ALL THE TIME?

NOT JUST TO YOU!

THE OTHER GLIDERS--

WHY WON'T YOU LET US STAY HERE IF WE WANT?

BECAUSE THIS IS MY HOME. IT BELONGS TO ME.

IT BELONGS TO ME!

HELPLESS, SUNTOP KNOWS THAT WINNOWILL CAN BLOCK HIS EVERY ATTEMPT TO SEND TO HIS FOLK ABOVE.

WHAT CAN I DO..?

MAYBE... MAYBE I CAN FIND SAVAH--

--AND SHE CAN HELP ME!

I HAVE TO TRY!

SAVAH...

SAVAH, I'M HERE...

WHERE ARE YOU..?

114

MOMENTS LATER... (GASP) BRAVE CHILD..! REMARKABLE CHILD--

--TO SEEK YOUR MOTHER OF MEMORY THROUGH *ME!*

WERE YOU OLDER AND BETTER TRAINED, YOUR EFFORTS WOULD NOT BE *FUTILE!* NOW YOUR SPIRIT IS LOST IN THE VOID--

--BUT YOUR *BODY* IS STILL MINE TO BARGAIN WITH.

SUCH A PRETTY CHILD... MILD AND WILD... A DESERT BLOSSOM!

HE CROSSED THE SANDY SEA... BECAUSE OF *YOU,* BECAUSE OF *ME*--

CAN YOU PART WITH THIS ONE, TOO --THIS SUNNY *SUNTOP* SON?

MY PLAN HAS NOT CHANGED, *TWO-EDGE.* I SUPPOSE I MUST THANK YOU FOR YOUR PART IN IT.

SUPPOSE...

SUPPOSE... SUPPOSE *THEY* COME FOR HIM? SUPPOSE THEY COME FOR YOU?

WHAT? GO AWAY!

SUCH IDLE TALK BORES ME. YOU KNOW BEST, SINCE MY MEANS OF ESCAPE WAS YOUR *FATHER'S* CREATION, THAT *NO ONE* CAN FOLLOW ME.

THEN WHY, OH, WHY DO LITTLE FEET CREEP IN THE TUNNEL OF GLOBES..?

116

NOT FAR... TO THE LAIR OF ONE WHO SENSES THAT ALL IS NOT AS SHE PLANNED.

TWO-EDGE MAY JUST BE PLAYING GAMES--

--BUT I DARE NOT TAKE THE CHANCE.

I HAVE ALLIES FAR MORE RELIABLE AND OBEDIENT THAN HE.

THE BLACK ROBED ELF WOMAN GLIDES TOWARD AN ORNATE PORTAL.

IT IS ANOTHER "DOOR"--

--OPENED AND CLOSED BY A SILENT ROCK SHAPER WHO HAS CHOSEN THIS AND NO OTHER PATH.

DOOR OPEN!

DOOR OPEN!

ACCUSTOMED TO INSTANT RESPONSE TO HER COMMANDS, WINNOWILL CALMLY WATCHES AS SOLID ROCK SEEMS TO MELT APART, REVEALING HER ADJOINING QUARTERS.

KAKUK, I HAVE NEED OF YOU AND THE OTHERS.

OUTSIDERS COME...! YOU MUST DEFEND ME, AND KEEP THEM AWAY FROM THIS CHILD!

A CHILD, MISTRESS...? A CHILD! HAVE THE BIRD SPIRITS AT LAST BEEN BLESSED WITH YOUNG OF THEIR OWN?

117

SEE HOW DARK HIS SKIN IS — LIKE OURS!

THAT IS A SIGN TO YOU, A SYMBOL OF THE ENDURING BOND BETWEEN BIRD SPIRITS AND HUMANS!

THE OUTSIDERS COME TO DESTROY THAT ANCIENT BOND! I HEAR THEM NOW! GET WEAPONS AND PREPARE TO FIGHT!

THE LIE STINGS HER PRIDE, FOR SHE HAS NEVER BEFORE RESORTED TO DECEPTION TO INSURE HER HUMANS' LOYALTY.

BUT TIME IS SHORT--

--THE "OUTSIDERS" ARE HERE!

OOOOO! BIGTHINGS! MANY BIGTHINGS!

STOP HUMANS!

WE HAVE NO QUARREL WITH YOU!

I ONLY WANT MY SON!

(GASP) BIRD SPIRITS — WHO SPEAK OUR LANGUAGE!

THEY ARE SO SMALL!

ARE THEY CHILDREN TOO..?

STUNNED, THE HUMANS HESITATE, UNSURE WHERE THEIR DUTY LIES.

WE CANNOT HARM CHILDREN OF THE BIRD SPIRITS!

WHY DID SHE COMMAND US TO? WHY?

YOU'RE RIGHT! WINNOWILL'S CRAZY!

SHE CARES NOTHING FOR YOU! YOU'RE JUST HER PETS! HER SLAVES!

DO NOT LISTEN, FOOLS — I AM YOUR MISTRESS!

YOUR DUTY IS TO ME!

ATTACK THEM!

RELUCTANTLY, BUT BECAUSE THEY HAVE ALWAYS DONE SO, THE HUMANS DO WINNOWILL'S BIDDING NOW. SLOWLY THEY ADVANCE ON THE WOLFRIDERS.

BUT CUTTER HAS LEARNED THERE ARE MANY WAY TO DEAL WITH HUMANS.

AND THE BEST WAY NOW--

--IS NOT TO DEAL WITH THEM AT ALL!

FOLLOW ME!

BY THE GIANT BIRDS!

THEY SWARM UP THE COLUMNS LIKE--

--ANTS!

THEY ARE TOO QUICK!

CUTTER NOTES THE RELIEF IN KAKUK'S WORDS AND COUNTS IT A STROKE OF LUCK.

COME ON! HURRY!

BIGTHINGS ALL FUSS FUSTED! HEE HEE!

CROSSING THE CURIOUS MESH OF HANGING VINES THE RESCUERS SPOT THEIR QUARRY.

THERE'S THE CUB STEALER!

BUT LOOK! LOOK AT SUNTOP!

WHAT HAS SHE DONE TO HIM?!

THESE VINES--

--THEY'VE BEEN SHAPED!

NO! THEY'RE NOT VINES AT ALL! THEY'RE--

119

--STRANGLEWEED!

OH NO!

@*!!!?*

I'M CAUGHT! WHAT IS HAPPENING?

STRANGLEWEED! ≡UNH≡ IT LIES ON THE GROUND, GRABS YOU AND SLOWLY CHOKES THE LIFE OUT OF YOU ≡UGH≡! THIS IS WORSE!

I OWE THANKS TO THE TREE-SHAPER WHO MADE ME THAT WEB... AND THEN DIED IN IT.

FARE WELL, WOLF-RIDERS!

NO! SHE'S TAKING SUNTOP AWAY!

CUTTER, I CAN STOP HER FAST! WANT ME TO..?

YES!

HURRY, REDLANCE! IF YOU EVER CONVINCED A VINE TO LET LOOSE--

-- GET MY ARMS FREE!

NOW?

NOW!

THAT'S MY CHIEF!

120

TURN, YOU MATE OF MADCOIL!

TURN AROUND, SHE SNAKE!

TURN!

FOR A LAST LOOK AT YOU IN PERIL? GLADLY--!

THUD!

WHA--?! YOU DIDN'T KILL HER!

I WANT TO...BUT IF SHE'S TANGLED SUNTOP'S BRAINS MAYBE ONLY SHE CAN UNTANGLE 'EM!

STRONGBOW CURSES ALOUD AS THE WEEDS ENSNARE HIS ARMS AGAIN. BUT BELOW, A DIFFERENT KIND OF STRUGGLE GOES ON.

SAVAH..?

SAVAH! OH, SAVAH! I FEEL YOU NEAR ME!

I AM NEAR, MY DEAR ONE. REST CALMLY. SOON WE SHALL BOTH BE FREE.

N-NO!

121

WINNOWILL TRIED TO OWN YOU! SHE'S EVIL! I KNOW WHAT THAT MEANS NOW.

THINK OF IT AS THE ABSENCE OF LOVE. THEN IT WILL NOT SEEM SO FRIGHTENING.

WINNOWILL NEEDS HEALING IN BODY AND IN MIND.

GASP!

LOOK! A DOOR! A DOOR IS OPENING FOR US!

FOR YOU, SUNTOP. GO BACK. GO BACK AND TELL LEETAH OF OUR MEETING.

SHE WILL KNOW WHAT TO DO.

OH, MISTRESS! LET ME HELP!

THEY—THEY WOUNDED YOU!

UNNOTICED, SUNTOP AWAKENS.

MOTHER! MOTHER! I'VE SEEN SAVAH!

MY CUBLING!

SHE SAYS WINNOWILL NEEDS HEALING!

SHE SAYS YOU CAN DO IT!

WE'LL HEAL HER ALL RIGHT! PETALWING!

WHACK!

GET BIGTHINGS! MAKE WRAPSTUFF!

WHEE!

AKK!

COUGH!

SPLUTTER!

YUGH!

LEAVE ME! YOUR CONCERN IS USELESS! I CAN HEAL MYSELF! GO AND FIGHT!

WINNOWILL, PLEASE GIVE UP! PLEASE!

UNH! MUST REACH MY DAGGER...!

THERE, SUNTOP! I'LL BE WITH YOU SOON, MY LITTLE ONE.

CUTTER'S FRIGHTENED PROTESTS CANNOT HALT LEETAH'S CARELESS, FRANTIC SLASHING OF THE VINES.

--FALL!

NO! WATCH OUT! LEETAH, YOU'LL--

MOTHER!

WINNOWILL GLARES AT HER SHAKEN OPPONENT... AND THEN--

OOHH... SUNTOP! I WANT MY SON!

--SHE WHIRLS AWAY TO THE SAFETY OF HER PRIVATE CHAMBERS--

--ONLY TO FIND--

CLOSED!

HOW CAN IT BE?!

WINNOWILL!

GIVE ME MY CHILD!

DOOR! I ORDERED YOU OPEN!

HOW DARE Y--?!

YOU...

TREMBLING, WEAK WITH PAIN, WINNOWILL FLEES FROM LEETAH.

SHE FEARS THE DESERT-BORN HEALER FOR REASONS SHE CANNOT NAME.

BAD! BAD! BAD!

LET ME BE, YOU WRETCHED CREATURE!

AT LAST! SHE'S TOO WEAK TO HOLD SUNTOP ANY LONGER!

BACK AWAY, LEETAH... YOU'VE DONE YOUR PART.

NO..! SAVAH TOLD SUNTOP ...I CAN HEAL HER!

I-I CAN TRY...

LET ME TRY, MY DEAR LIFE-MATE!

D-DO NOT TOUCH ME...!

I WILL. YOU HAVE MORE TO FEAR THAN I.

SOFT, BROWN HANDS CARESS PEARLY FLESH, CLOSE UPON A WOUND MUCH DEEPER THAN BLOOD, MUSCLE OR BONE.

EVEN AS IT SOOTHES, THE TOUCH BURNS WITH ITS SEARING PURITY.

WINNOWILL, WHO MOCKED THE WOLF-RIDERS' TAINTED BLOOD, CAN-NOT BEAR THE BLAZING REALITY OF ALL THAT A TRUE HEALER CAN BE.

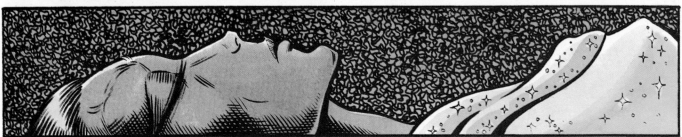

SHE, HERSELF IS TAINTED— BY CHOICE.

BUT ALL THAT SHE HAS BECOME WILL CHANGE...

...UNLESS SHE MAKES THE FINAL CHOICE...

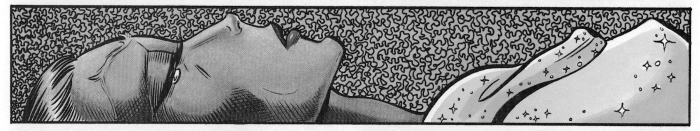

OOH!

WINNOWILL!

TIMMORN'S BLOOD!

SHE... JUST STEPPED OFF... THE EDGE!

FREE.

HEH HEH HEH HEH HEH...

—WHERE ARE HIS BONES..? MY FATHER'S BONES...

T-TWO EDGE... HELP ME...

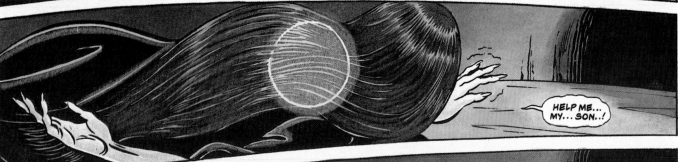

HELP ME... MY... SON..!

FIND US BOTH, MY TREASURE AND ME...

THE SWORD IS THE KEY... THE SWORD IS THE KEY...

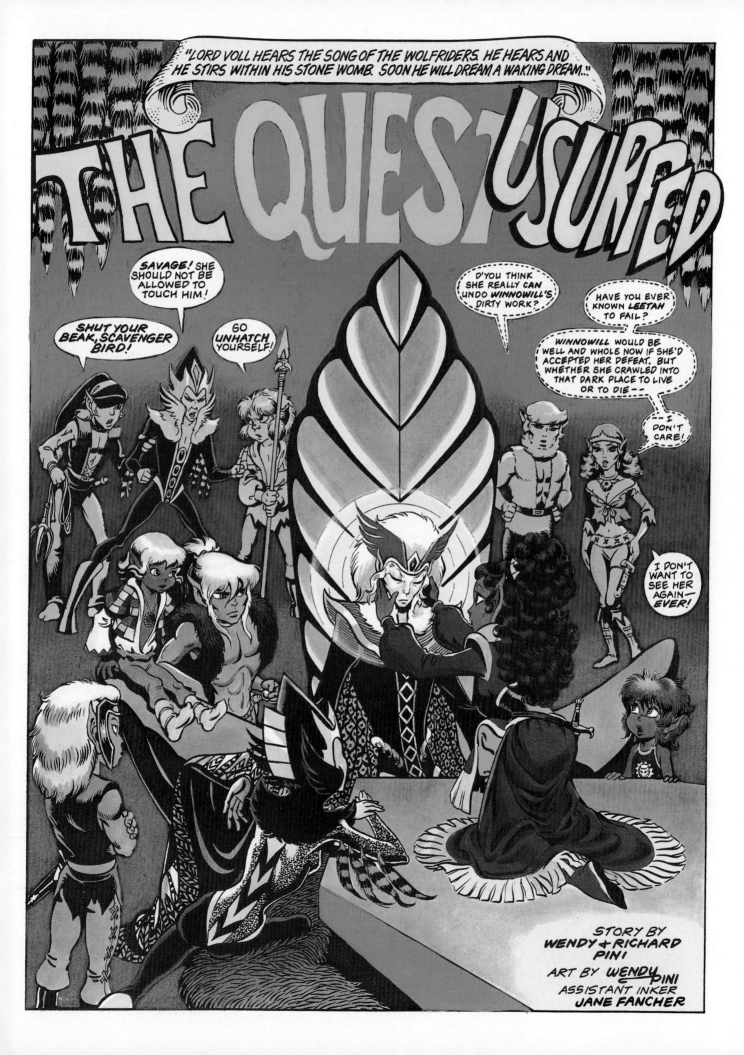

COME, GENTLE LORD... OPEN YOUR EYES!

MMM... MPH...

NO! STOP THIS SHAMEFUL BRAWLING...! KUREEL! TYLDAK! WHA--?!

WH--WHAT'S HAPPENED?

WINNOWILL PUT YOU TO SLEEP, LORD VOLL, SO THAT YOU COULD NOT INTERFERE WITH HER PLANS!

PLANS?

THE WOLFRIDERS NEARLY FALL OVER ONE ANOTHER IN THEIR HASTE TO TELL VOLL OF WINNOWILL'S EVERY CRUEL MANIPULATION--

--FROM THE TORTURE OF STRONGBOW TO THE KIDNAPPING OF SUNTOP!

--SHE TRIED TO FORCE US TO LEAVE BLUE MOUNTAIN IN EXCHANGE FOR THE CUB'S RETURN!

BUT SHE KNEW YOU'D NEVER LET HER GET AWAY WITH IT--

--SO SHE TURNED HER POWERS AGAINST ME! EVEN ME! BUT WHY? WHY SUCH DESPERATION TO DRIVE YOU WOLFRIDERS AWAY?

WHAT WAS HER TERRIBLE FEAR?

NOTHING MORE TERRIBLE--

--THAN THIS!

PETALWING... SAY HELLO TO LORD VOLL!

HELLO! HELLO! HELLO!

OLD OLD HIGHTHING REMEMBER PETALWING?

I-I CAN HARDLY BELIEVE MY EYES!

BUT LOOK, LOOK MY PEOPLE...

A PRESERVER!

130

WHAT EVER HAPPENED TO YOU, LITTLE HELPER?

WE FOUND **PETALWING** AND ITS FRIENDS IN THE WOODS.

THE WOODS..? BUT WHY DID THE WINGED ONES DESERT US TO LIVE OUTSIDE?

PROTECT? WHAT FROM?

WINNOWILL TOLD ME *SHE* SENT THE PER-PRESERVERS AWAY A LONG TIME AGO... TO PROTECT *YOU* SHE SAID.

WHAT'D SHE MEAN?

"TO PROTECT ME?" MURMURS **LORD VOLL**. "OH, **WINNOWILL**! HOW LONG IT HAS BEEN SINCE WE UNDERSTOOD ONE ANOTHER!"

"I TELL YOU, WOLFRIDERS, THERE WAS A TIME WHEN **WINNOWILL** WAS ALL THE REASON I NEEDED TO BELIEVE IN MYSELF. SHE WAS FRIEND, LOVEMATE, ADVISOR... MY STEADFAST SUPPORTER WHEN OTHERS TURNED THEIR BACKS ON ME. I BELIEVED IT WAS MY DESTINY TO GUIDE ALL ELVES BACK TO THE WAYS OF THE FIRSTCOMERS --"

"--AND **WINNOWILL** WAS NO LESS DEVOTED TO THAT DREAM THAN I. TOGETHER WE WATCHED WITH PRIDE AS BLUE MOUNTAIN BECAME A WORLD UNTO ITSELF, SHAPED AND MOLDED BY THE EVER IMPROVING POWERS OF OUR FOLLOWERS."

"SHE HELPED ME TO ACHIEVE MY DREAM..."

"BUT SOMETHING HAPPENED TO HER, TO ALL OF US. **WINNOWILL** VANISHED FOR A TIME, DEEP WITHIN THE ROOTS OF THE MOUNTAIN, NO ONE COULD FIND HER. WHEN SHE RETURNED, SHE WAS MUCH AS YOU KNOW HER NOW. WHAT CAUSED HER GRIM CHANGE --"

--I CANNOT SAY. BUT THE DREAM IS *DYING* ...DYING EVEN AS IT LIVES ON.

131

AND I DO NOT KNOW WHY.

I DO! A STARVING ANIMAL TRAPPED IN A PIT WILL GNAW AT ITS *OWN BODY* RATHER THAN DIE OF HUNGER!

YOU GLIDERS HAVE BEEN *FEEDING* ON YOURSELVES--

--FOR WHO KNOWS *HOW LONG!*

THIS MOUNTAIN CAN HOLD JUST SO MANY. THAT'S WHY YOU DON'T *BREED* ANY MORE!

THAT'S WHY--

EH?

DEWSHINE!

WHAT IS *WRONG* WITH HER?

IS SHE *ILL?*

SHE IS--

MY POOR CUB!

--BECAUSE SHE'S FIGHTING *RECOGNITION!*

RECOGNITION?!!

WITH WHOM?

THE WOLFRIDERS LOOK UP, A STRANGE BLEND OF PITY AND BLAME IN THEIR EYES.

THE WINGED ELF'S SHAKY LANDING PROVES THAT HE, TOO, FEELS THE INESCAPABLE EFFECTS OF RECOGNITION DENIED!

TYLDAK?!

SHE HAS RECOGNIZED ONE OF *MY OWN?*

IS THIS *TRUE?*

IT IS... *TRUE,* MY LORD.

BUT I WANT HER AS LITTLE AS SHE WANTS ME!

THIS IS AN *OUTRAGE* TO *BOTH* OF US!

BUT *TYLDAK*, RECOGNITION HAS NOT HAPPENED AMONG THE GLIDERS FOR FAR TOO LONG!

THIS IS NO OUT-RAGE — IT IS A *BLESSING!*

PLEASE ACCEPT IT!

YOU CANNOT KNOW WHAT THIS MEANS TO ME!

EVEN IF *I* ACCEPT--

--I WILL *NOT!!* MY LIFE IS WITH THE *WOLFRIDERS!*

I WON'T STAY HERE! AND I WON'T LEAVE *SCOUTER!*

OH, KITLING... IN THE END RECOGNITION IS A COMMAND THAT *NO* ELF CAN DEFY!

IT MEANS NEW LIFE!

AND THINK, THERE ARE TOO FEW OF US AS IT IS!

DEWSHINE... I MAKE YOU A *PROMISE.*

IF *TYLDAK* WON'T BE A FATHER TO THE CUB YOU MUST BEAR --

--*I* WILL!

AND WHETHER IT HAS WINGS--

--OR YOUR WHITE GOLD HAIR AND BEAUTIFUL EYES--

--I'LL LOVE IT--

-- BECAUSE IT WILL BE A PART OF *YOU!*

WHEN WAS THE LAST TIME SUCH TENDERNESS GRACED OUR EXISTENCE, *TYLDAK--?*

--DO YOU NOT *ENVY* THEM, THESE "SAVAGES" FROM THE WORLD OUTSIDE?

DEWSHINE TURNS--

133

AND...

WE... CAN'T BE LIFEMATES.

I KNOW...

AS HE SEES HER--

--SO SHE SEES HIM.

BUT WE CAN SET EACH OTHER FREE.

YOU KNOW, ONE-EYE... SCOUTER'S ABOUT THE SAME AGE I WAS WHEN I FIRST JOINED WITH LEETAH.

BUT HE'S PUTTING UP WITH TYLDAK A LOT BETTER THAN I PUT UP WITH RAYEK!

(SOB)

WHAT IS IT?

FROM HER BODICE, LEETAH DRAWS A SMALL OBJECT--

--A FINGER BONE! TEARS SLIDE SOFTLY DOWN HER CHEEKS AS SHE TELLS. CUTTER OF THE OPEN TOMB IN THE DESERT AND THE PATHETIC REMAINS SHE FOUND THERE.

AND YOU THINK... THIS IS..?

IT MUST BE!

BARE OF FLESH FOR ONLY A FEW YEARS SINCE HE CROSSED THE DESERT... PERHAPS HIS WATER AND HIS FOOD RAN OUT... PERHAPS HE ONLY HAD STRENGTH ENOUGH TO LEVITATE THE HOT STONES... TO CRAWL OUT OF THE SUN INTO THAT SMALL CAVE... AND THEN...(CHOKE)

RAYEK...! I'M SORRY. I REALLY AM ...SORRY.

134

135

I'VE FAILED TO LEAD MY CHILDREN ON THE PATH OF THE FIRST-COMERS!

WE ARE *NOT* THE HIGH ONES! OUR LIVES HAVE BEEN BUT A POOR *IMITATION* OF THEIR WAYS!

I KNEW IT! I KNEW IT!!

SIGH...

NO MOUNTAIN COULD EVER MATCH THE *TRUE* DWELLING OF THE *HIGH ONES*... IT WAS AN AWESOME STRUCTURE— A *PALACE* — ALIVE WITH SUCH MAGIC AS YOU CAN- NOT CONCEIVE!

I REMEMBER... OH, I REMEMBER NOW, THE TALES MY PARENTS TOLD!

I REMEMBER THEIR SENDINGS, RICH IN IMAGES OF THOSE CRYSTALINE SPIRES AND HIGH, SHIMMERING WALLS!

IT WAS A VESSEL OF POWER FAR BEYOND ANYTHING WE CALL MAGIC NOW —

OLD OLD HIGHTHING WANT GO HOMEPLACE?

—AND, TO THINK THAT THE HUMANS' WEAPONS AND IGNORANCE WERE MORE POWERFUL STILL...! POWER- FUL ENOUGH TO DRIVE THE *HIGH ONES* AWAY—

—AND PREVENT THEM FROM EVER RETURNING TO THEIR RIGHTFUL ABODE!

PETALWING TAKE HIGH~ THINGS HOME!

HA HA HA

OH *SURE!* LET'S ALL FOLLOW A LITTLE TALKING BUG —

—TO THE LOST DWELL- ING OF THE *HIGH ONES!*

YOU CAN GET THERE FASTER ON A BELLY FULL OF OVER-RIPE *DREAMBERRIES!*

I KNOW! I'VE DONE IT LOT'S OF TIMES!

NO LAUGH, ROSYNOSE HIGHTHING!

PETALWING KNOWS! PETALWING SAY SO!

HIGHTHINGS WANT GO CASTLE? PETALWING DO!

CURSE MY LOST EYE, BUT I'D SWEAR THE BUG WAS *SERIOUS!*

HA HA HA HA HA

HA HA HA HA

I REALIZED EVEN AS WE MADE A LIFE FOR OURSELVES HERE-- --THAT BLUE MOUNTAIN WAS MERELY A SUBSTITUTE FOR OUR FIRST AND BEST HOME! WINNOWILL'S MISGUIDED PROTECTIVENESS CANNOT HINDER ME AGAIN! I WILL FIND IT--

WOA! SLOW DOWN!

WE DON'T EVEN KNOW IF THE -- WHAT DID YOU CALL IT -- ? PALACE STILL EXISTS!

CAN YOU DOUBT? WE EXIST DESPITE ALL THIS WORLD'S EFFORTS TO CRUSH US!

IF WE SURVIVED HEAT AND COLD, PREDATORS, TIME AND EVEN HUMANS--

HEE HEE HEE!

--WHY SHOULD NOT THE PALACE STILL BE THERE?

COME SEEK IT WITH ME, BRAVE WOLFRIDERS! YOU HAVE THE STRENGTH AND NOW WE HAVE OUR GUIDE!

I DON'T KNOW, VOLL...

I DON'T KNOW...

LATER...AS CUTTER PONDERS HIS NEXT DECISION...

YOU KNOW, IT'S BEEN A WHILE SINCE WE WATCHED THE STARS TOGETHER.

YOU'RE RIGHT. SO MUCH HAS HAPPENED, THERE'S BEEN NO TIME.

WE'LL MAKE THE TIME! LET'S GO!

ALL RIGHT.

LET STAR-JUMPER COME TOO.

I LIKE HIS SMELL.

CUTTER AND SKYWISE CLIMB UP TO THE AERIE. THE SCENT AND MOISTNESS OF RECENT RAIN STILL LINGER IN THE AIR.

YOU'RE NOT AFRAID TO LOOK DOWN!

MY MIND'S TOO FULL OF THOUGHTS FOR FEAR.

I SEE THINGS SO DIFFERENTLY NOW...

EVERYTHING'S CHANGED.

138

NOT *EVERYTHING*. JUST YOU... AND ME. YOU'VE BECOME A REAL CHIEF. EVEN *STRONGBOW* ADMITS IT. HE'S THE KIND THAT *WANTS* TO BE TOLD WHAT TO DO.

I NEVER UNDERSTOOD THAT BEFORE.

IN COUNCIL I'VE ALWAYS TRIED TO HEAR EVERY VOICE...TO MAKE DECISIONS THAT WOULD PLEASE EVERYONE.

BUT YOU KNOW SOMETHING? LISTENING TOO MUCH IS AS BAD AS BEING *DEAF!*

THERE'S A TIME TO ASK OPINIONS AND A TIME TO GIVE ORDERS--

--AND NOW I KNOW THE DIFFERENCE.

WHAT ABOUT *YOU?*

I'VE BEEN UP THERE...*FLYING.* I'VE ALWAYS DREAMED OF BEING ABLE TO. NOW I'VE SEEN THE WORLD AS THE STARS SEE IT-- FROM A GREAT HEIGHT.

BUT I STILL COULDN'T *TOUCH* THE STARS.

YOU ALREADY HAVE! WHAT'S *THIS* AFTER ALL, AN OWL PELLET?

IT'S A *KEY*--

--LIKE THE ONE IN YOUR *SWORD.* YOURS OPENS THE WAY TO *TWO-EDGE'S* GOLDEN TREASURE.

MINE POINTS THE WAY TO ... *WHAT?*

TO A CRAZY DREAM--

--OR TO THE LOST DWELLING OF THE *HIGH* ONES?

WILL WE EVER KNOW?

NOW YOU SOUND LIKE *ME!*

TERRIBLE THOUGHT!

HEH HEH HEH MRPH HEH

(HEH HEH) SOMEDAY, FRIEND, SOMEDAY... MAYBE WHEN *EMBER'S* GROWN AND CAN LEAD THE TRIBE IN MY PLACE--

--THEN YOU AND I WILL FOLLOW THE LODESTONE AGAIN. BUT THE GLIDERS HAVE SHOWN ME THAT ALL ELVES ARE *NOT* OF ONE HEART AND ONE MIND.

I'LL SAY! WE FOUND MORE THAN WE BARGAINED FOR IN BLUE MOUNTAIN!

BUT WHAT ABOUT THE QUEST...?

IT'S TIME TO STOP AND THINK OVER THE *REASON* FOR IT--

--IN A *NEW HOLT,* MAYBE, WITH A NEW *WOLF* FRIEND BY MY SIDE.

I'VE DECIDED--

"--THE WOLFRIDERS WILL RETURN TO THE WOODS!"

CUTTER, I ENTREAT YOU, RECONSIDER! *YOU,* WHO SET OUT TO FIND AND UNITE THE SCATTERED DESCENDANTS OF THE *HIGH ONES--*

--*YOU,* WHO PATIENTLY OFFERED THE HAND OF FRIENDSHIP THOUGH WE GLIDERS REPEATEDLY SLAPPED IT ASIDE --

-- YOU ABOVE ALL SHOULD BE ABLE TO SHARE MY VISION NOW! IT IS YOUR NATURE, YOUNG CHIEFTAIN, AND YOUR DESTINY!

I STILL BELIEVE IN THE QUEST, *LORD VOLL,* AND IF THE RISK WERE MINE ALONE, I'D FOLLOW YOU IN AN INSTANT!

IT WOULD BE *WONDERFUL* TO FIND THE PALACE.

BUT I CAN'T ASK MY TRIBE TO RISK EVERYTHING FOR A VISION! *THEY COME FIRST!*

MAYBE *YOU'VE* FOR-GOTTEN HOW THE SEASONS TURN--

--BUT I SCENTED THE *DEATH-SLEEP* ON THE WIND JUST NOW. WE MUST SETTLE IN A *NEW HOLT* BEFORE THE LEAVES FALL AND THE WHITE COLD COMES.

YOU WILL GO *HUNGRY!* YOU WILL *FREEZE!*

HA HA HA HA HA! SO WE'D BE BETTER OFF CHASING AFTER THE *HIGH ONES'* MOUNTAIN THING WITH *YOU!?*

(SIGH) VERY WELL...

THOUGH YOU DISAPPOINT ME BEYOND MEASURE, I SHALL NOT PRESS FURTHER.

BUT IF YOU INTEND TO LEAVE NOW, AT LEAST LET MY PARTING GIFTS MAKE AMENDS FOR ALL YOU HAVE SUFFERED HERE.

AND SO...

I DON'T KNOW WHAT STRANGE BEAST WORE THIS FUR BEFORE YOU, LEETAH, BUT YOU WEAR IT WELL NOW!

AYE! VERY WELL! AND IT'LL KEEP THE WHITE COLD FROM GNAWING AT YOUR PRETTY BONES TOO! YOU'LL SEE!

ME, I LIKE THE SNOW! I'VE MISSED IT THESE SEVEN TURNS OF THE SEASONS.

EMBER!

ME TOO!

HOW CAN YOU MISS SOMETHING YOU'VE NEVER SEEN?

OH, FATHERRR...! YOU GAVE US SOME SENDING PICTURES, REMEMBER?

SNOW LOOKS LIKE SAND, 'CEPT ITS WHITE, WHITE, WHITE!

RRRIGHT, SUNTOP?

ARE YOU SORRY WE WON'T BE RETURNING SOON TO SORROW'S END, BELOVED?

SAVAH IS FREE ...RAINSONG CARRIES A NEW HEALER...DART AND WOODLOCK TEACH MY FOLK TO PROTECT THEM-SELVES.

I HAVE NO FEARS.

AND AS FOR LEARNING MORE ABOUT OUR ANCESTORS--

--THERE IS PLENTY OF TIME FOR THAT.

I KNOW WE HAVE NOT SEEN THE LAST OF LORD VOLL.

YES...PLENTY OF TIME. MY QUEST WAS SUPPOSED TO BE DONE IN ONLY ONE YEAR. BUT NOW I THINK IT WILL GO ON AS LONG AS I LIVE.

NOW, STRONGBOW, ONE LAST TIME—GET US OUT OF HERE!

WHAT ABOUT DEWSHINE?

FEARING THAT HE MIGHT INTRUDE ON HER PRIVACY, YET LOATHE TO LEAVE WITHOUT KNOWING WHERE SHE IS, SCOUTER SENDS--

--AND IS ANSWERED!

LISTEN, EVERY-ONE!

DEWSHINE WANTS US TO COME TO THE AERIE! SOMETHING'S HAPPENED!

MOMENTS LATER...

WHAT A CROWD!

WHAT'S GOING ON?

ONE SIDE!

SKYWISE, COME LOOK! LORD VOLL FLIES!!

HE WHAT?

THE WOLFRIDERS STARE IN ADMIRATION. DESPITE HIS GREAT AGE AND SEEMING FRAILTY, THE GLIDERS' LORD MASTERS HIS AVIAN MOUNT AS THOUGH HE WERE ONCE AGAIN A BOLD LEADER PROVIDING FOR HIS PEOPLE.

HE RIDES UPON TENSPAN, THE OLDEST AND WILDEST OF THE GREAT BIRDS!

A TIME LONG GONE IS BORN ANEW!

REMEMBER HOW IT WAS WHEN OUR GOOD VOLL SET US ALL ABLAZE WITH THE FLAME OF HIS VISION?

AROREE! WHAT ARE YOU DOING?

MY LORD SENDS TO ME...

I AM ONE OF *HIS CHOSEN!*

I AM HIS TO COMMAND!

ENOUGH, *VOLL!* LAND THIS BIRD *NOW!*

NO! IF THE WOLFRIDERS WILL NOT SEEK THEIR *RIGHTFUL* HERITAGE BY CHOICE--

--THEN I MUST *FORCE* THEM TO FOLLOW ME!

YOU MAY HATE ME NOW, YOUNG CHIEF, BUT WHEN YOU STAND BEFORE THE PALACE OF THE *HIGH ONES,* YOU WILL BE GLAD I TOOK SUCH ACTION.

I'LL TAKE YOUR *THROAT* OUT, YOU *DECEIVER!*

YOU'RE *WORSE* THAN *WINNOWILL!!*

WE TRUSTED YOU LIKE A *FATHER!*

I KNOW... BUT YOU CAN DO NOTHING. KILL ME, AND *TENSPAN* WILL HURL YOU BOTH TO THE GROUND! ONLY *I* CAN FLY HIM.

BELIEVE ME, *CUTTER.* WHAT I DO IS FOR THE BEST.

CONTROLLING HIS PANIC, CUTTER TURNS AND SEES--

--*TYLDAK!* THE OTHERS ARE OUT OF SENDING RANGE, BUT *HE* ISN'T!

TYLDAK, GET BACK TO THE WOLFRIDERS!

TELL THEM NOT TO FOLLOW! SAY I *ORDER* THEM TO STAY IN THE WOODS! HURRY!

UNABLE TO MATCH THE GIANT BIRDS' SPEED, THE WINGED ELF VEERS OFF AND HEADS BACK TO BLUE MOUNTAIN.

CUTTER'S COMMAND IS GIVEN--

AND THE WOLFRIDERS OBEY--
--IN THE ONLY WAY THEIR LOYALTY WILL ALLOW.

AYOOOOAAAH!

AROREE...WHY ARE YOU HELPING VOLL...?

AND VOLL..! CURSE HIM! WHO CAN WE TRUST--

--IF NOT THE HIGH ONES' FIRST BORN?

LOOK! THE BIRDS ARE CIRCLING! WAITING FOR US!

THEY WANT US TO FOLLOW!

AH, GOOD! I KNEW, JUST AS YOU SURELY KNEW IN YOUR HEART, THAT YOUR TRIBEFOLK WOULD NOT ABANDON YOU.

NO!

NOW, PETAL-WING--

--TAKE US HOME!

OBLIVIOUS TO CUTTER AND LEETAH'S PROTESTS, EAGER TO PERFORM ITS MOST DEEPLY INGRAINED FUNCTION, THE TINY PRESERVER FLIES JUST AHEAD OF TENSPAN'S HUGE BEAK.

ABLE, NOW, TO KEEP UP WITH THE SLOWER, CIRCLING PATTERN, TYLDAK JOINS THE CHASE—

—AS DOES KUREEL—

—WHO, HIS OWN MOUNT SLAIN, RIDES DOUBLE WITH ANOTHER OF THE CHOSEN EIGHT.

DURABLE RUNNERS, THE WOLVES COVER GREAT DISTANCES ALWAYS KEEPING THEIR SKY-BOUND PREY IN SIGHT.

SPURRED BY THEIR ELF-FRIENDS' FURY AND OUTRAGE, THE POWERFUL CANINES GIVE THEIR ALL.

BUT WHEN NIGHT FALLS, AND THE GLIDERS DISAPPEAR AGAINST THE BLACK SKY—

—IT IS THE LODESTONE WHICH LEADS THE WAY—

—A CAUTIOUS, CAREFUL WAY, FOR THE LAND IS NEW AND STRANGE.

AWARE OF THE LIMITS OF THE ANIMALS' STRENGTH, VOLL ALLOWS TIMES FOR REST. ON THE SECOND DAY OF THEIR UNWANTED JOURNEY, CUTTER AND HIS FAMILY FIND THEMSELVES HIGH ATOP A CRAGGY PEAK.

THEY ARE CLOSELY GUARDED BY VOLL'S THREE ESCORTS WHILE TYLDAK HUNTS FOR FOOD. AGAIN AND AGAIN THE CAPTIVES DEMAND THEIR FREEDOM.

AND WHEN THEIR DEMANDS FAIL THEY TRY CALM, REASONED ENTREATIES—

—ALL TO NO AVAIL.

VOLL'S BELIEF IN HIS MISSION REMAINS UNSHAKABLE, THOUGH HIS USE OF FORCE GRIEVES HIM.

THE ACHE IN HIS BREAST, HE TELLS HIMSELF, IS PAYMENT ENOUGH.

OTHERS, TOO, FEEL PANGS OF GUILT—

—AND SEEK TO EXPLAIN THEMSELVES.

OH, MY CLEVER, CURIOUS SKYWISE, DON'T YOU SEE? YOU WERE RIGHT!

WHEN VOLL CALLED ME TO SEEK THE PALACE WITH HIM I OBEYED GLADLY... INSTANTLY! BECAUSE YOU HAVE OPENED MY EYES!

147

YOU'VE MADE ME FEEL *ALIVE* AGAIN! I WANT MORE AND MORE OF THAT FEELING! SHOULD I NOT BE AS BRAVE AND ADVENTUROUS AS *YOU*?

NOT IF IT COSTS MY FRIENDS' LIVES! YOU *ABDUCTED* THEM--

--WITHOUT A SINGLE THOUGHT FOR THEIR SAFETY!

WRONG!

VOLL WANTS ONLY WHAT IS *BEST* FOR *ALL* OF US!

HE IS OUR *LORD* ...OUR "CHIEF--"

--A MUCH *GREATER* CHIEF THAN *YOURS!* HAD YOU ONLY FOLLOWED *VOLL* WHEN HE *ASKED*, THIS WOULD NOT HAVE BEEN NECESSARY.

THAT SO?

WELL, WE CAN TAKE HOSTAGES *TOO!*

JUST BEFORE VIOLENCE ERUPTS, AN OPEN SENDING, UNLIKE ANY THE WOLFRIDERS HAVE YET EXPERIENCED, LANCES DOWN FROM THE LOOMING CRAGS.

MY CHILDREN, YOU MUST *SEE* AND *KNOW* WHAT IT IS THAT I OFFER YOU!

CASTLE...PALACE...HOMEPLACE... LOST DWELLING...MOUNTAIN THING.... ALL JUST WORDS TO WHICH THE SIMPLE, EARTHY WOLFRIDERS HAVE NEVER BEEN ABLE TO ATTACH AN IMAGE.

SUDDENLY THEY *FEEL* AS WELL AS *SEE* THAT THING OF MISTY LEGEND WHICH FIRST HOUSED THE *HIGH ONES*... THAT THING WHICH *BELONGS* TO ALL THEIR RACE BY BIRTHRIGHT.

AND BECAUSE THEY SEE IT WITH THEIR *HEARTS* AS WELL AS THEIR *MINDS*, THE PALACE APPEARS AS THE *HOLT OF HOLTS*— THE ULTIMATE REFUGE FOR A TRIBE WHOSE ONLY GOAL HAS EVER BEEN *SURVIVAL*.

EVEN *CUTTER'S* ANGER AND SENSE OF BETRAYAL BEGINS TO FADE BENEATH THE OVERWHELMING POIGNANCE OF *VOLL'S* IMAGERY. SINCE SENDINGS CANNOT CONTAIN LIES, THE WOLFRIDERS KNOW THEY ARE NOT, NOW, BEING LURED BY DECEPTION.

AND SO...

FOR SEVERAL MORE DAYS THE PURSUIT CONTINUES OVER TERRAIN THAT GROWS INCREASINGLY BLEAK AND BITTER WITH COLD. BUT THE WOLFRIDERS ARE SUSTAINED BY MORE THAN A VERY REAL DESIRE TO RESCUE THEIR CHIEF.

THEY HAVE SEEN THE PALACE OF THE HIGH ONES—

—AND NOW, FINALLY, THEY SENSE ITS PRESENCE SOMEWHERE BEHIND A RANGE OF SNOW-COVERED MOUNTAINS.

CAPTIVES THOUGH THEY ARE, *CUTTER* AND *LEETAH* SMILE IN ANTICIPATION.

HEE HEE

HOMEPLACE SOON!

THE FROZEN MOUNTAINS... MAJESTIC AND DAZZLING WHITE, EVEN ON THIS GRAY, SUNLESS DAY.

REARING SKYWARD, THE STEEP, ICY BARRIER DAUNTS THE SMALL BAND OF RIDERS—

—BUT NOT SO THE LORD OF THE *GLIDERS*, WHO IS ABLE TO SOAR HIGH AND SEE BEYOND THE PEAKS. VISIBLE ONLY TO *VOLL*, SON OF TRUE HIGH ONES, IS A SOFTLY GLOWING AURORA...

THERE, MY YOUNG FRIENDS... DON'T YOU SEE IT..?

THE *POWER* I SPOKE OF—

—THE MAGICAL *AURA* OF THE PALACE! SEE HOW IT WELCOMES US AFTER OUR AGE-LONG ABSENCE!

I SEE NOTHING, BUT I—I *KNOW* SOMETHING'S THERE!

TOK TOK TOK

IT IS THERE! IT IS!

THE PALACE! IS THIS NOT WORTH THE SMALL DISCOMFORTS I HAVE CAUSED YOU?

SOON WE SHALL BE HOME AND NOTHING—NO ONE—CAN DRIVE US AWAY FROM IT AGAIN!

THUNGG!

AAWNK!

EEE!!

TINK!

VOLL! OH, LORD VOLL!

THE WOLFRIDERS STAND QUIETLY, TOO STUNNED, YET, TO MOURN. THEIR FEW DAYS SPENT INSIDE THE MYSTERIOUS BLUE MOUNTAIN SEEM BUT A DREAM...A DREAM WHICH HAS SUDDENLY, SHOCKINGLY *DIED!*

AS NEVER BEFORE *CUTTER* REALIZES THE DANGER WHICH LIES IN BECOMING THE SLAVE RATHER THAN THE MASTER OF ONE'S DREAMS.

FOR THE FIRST TIME HE REGRETS EVER EMBARKING ON HIS QUEST.

REMORSE TOUCHES *SKYWISE* TOO, FOR THE FLAME HE HAD HELPED REKINDLE--

--HAS GONE OUT OF *ARORE'S* EYES... PERHAPS FOREVER.

BUT HOW? HOW DID THIS HAPPEN? WHERE DID THE LONG SPEAR COME FROM?

WHERE--?!

AAAA!

"THEY'VE CHANGED, THOSE TROLLS FROM THE FROZEN MOUNTAINS...!"

CUTTER AND *SKYWISE* GRIP THEIR SWORD HILTS, REMEMBERING *PICKNOSE'S* SINISTER WORDS. NOW THE ELVES SEE FOR THEMSELVES THAT THEIR OLD ENEMY DID NOT EXAGGERATE!

HOW DIFFERENT ARE THESE HULKING WARRIORS FROM *GREYMUNG'S* LUMPISH SUBJECTS!

151

152

153

155

CUTTER'S SPEED PROVES SUPERIOR. BUT EVEN AS ONE FOE FALLS--

--ANOTHER SEIZES THE CHANCE--

--TO STRIKE!

HIGH ONES NO!!

HE'S PINNED!

ABOVE THE DIN OF BATTLE HE HEARS A VOICE—LEETAH'S—SCREAMING HIS NAME!

SHE STILL LIVES. FROM THAT, AT LEAST, HE TAKES COMFORT.

THE TROLL GRINS...

HE WILL TWIST HIS SPEAR IN THE WOUND BEFORE GUTTING HIS VICTIM!

THAK!

UHHH...*

156

CUTTER!

SPLTCH!

SKYWISE BREAKS OFF THE BARBED TIP AND HELPS WITHDRAW THE SPEAR. IT IS **AGONY** FOR BOTH FRIENDS.

BRING HIM HERE! **HURRY!**

DON'T WASTE TIME ON ME *ⱿCOUGH!* KEEP FIGHTING!

THE HEALER FEELS IT IN THE TOUCH OF HER LIFEMATE'S HAND...

HE'S **DYING!** OH, MY **TAM!**

COME ON! CLIMB!

WAIT..! THE OTHERS!

RED AND WHITE, BLOOD AND SNOW... WITH FADING SIGHT, **CUTTER** GLIMPSES INSTANTS OF HORROR — **NIGHTFALL,** WOUNDED, HAMSTRINGS AN UNWARY FOE — **ONE-EYE,** HIS SWORD CAUGHT IN TROLL BONE, STRUGGLES TO FREE IT AS **DEATH** MOVES IN ON HIS BLIND SIDE!

ONE-EYE! NO! I–I CAN'T STAY HERE WHILE––

DO WHAT YOU HAVE TO. I'LL PROTECT LEETAH AND THE CUBS.

FAHR...

TAM...

THE EXCHANGE OF SOUL NAMES IS FAREWELL ENOUGH. THERE IS NO TIME FOR MORE.

TAM, I BEG YOU, COME TO ME! LET ME HEAL YOU!

...YOU MUST LIVE FOR ME, BELOVED... AND IF YOU DO, GET TO THE HOME OF THE HIGH ONES––

––I WILL SEE IT THROUGH YOUR EYES...

...YOURS AND... OUR CUBS!

NOOOO!!

AYOOOH!

CLEARBROOK!!

159

The Quest Concludes In

ElfQuest
BOOK 4

Afterwords

It is singularly appropriate that Boris Vallejo should write an introduction to this **ElfQuest Book 3**. Boris and his wife, Doris, were there in the beginning, when **ElfQuest** had barely gotten off the ground as an independent, black-and-white comic published by the newly minted mom-and-pop company, WaRP Graphics.

Themselves a husband/wife creative team, the Vallejos were there with encouragement, advice, and sometimes even commiseration as **ElfQuest** carved its self-defining niche in the world of graphic storytelling. Though years sometimes separated our visits with them, we were always grateful for the Vallejos' kind interest and their ability to find merit in our efforts. If any couple is qualified to speak with authority on the pressures and satisfactions success can bring, it is surely Boris and Doris.

Actually, we've been extremely fortunate over the past three years of color volumes, in that some of the brightest stars in the firmaments over both mainstream comics and science fiction/fantasy have shed their lights on us through their introductions. Some names carry the weight of much and justly deserved renown: Poul Anderson, Andre Norton, Boris Vallejo. Other names are less familiar to those who do not read comics, but within their sphere, they are names to reckon with: Marv Wolfman—writer, editor, creator, in large part responsible for Marvel Comics' *Tomb of Dracula* and DC Comics' *New Teen Titans;* C. C. Beck—creator of the original Captain Marvel and one of the chief exponents of the "Golden Age" of comics; Mary Jo Duffy—one of the few women forging a career in the American comics industry, assistant editor for *Epic Illustrated,* currently best known for her plots and scripts for Marvel's *Star Wars* series; and Frank Thorne—long-time comic and newspaper strip artist and writer, now producing his own epic graphic novel, *Ghita of Alizarr.* Add to this list Lynn Abbey, whose fantasy novels of the woman-warrior Rifkind have firmly established her in the science fiction and fantasy constellation, and one significant factor emerges: **ElfQuest** has bridged the gap between comics and science fiction/fantasy readers.

For a long time comics and science fiction fans regarded each others' choice of entertainment with barely disguised suspicion. Comics have always had to struggle, in this country, against an unsavory reputation, whereas in Europe graphic storytelling is regarded as an adult art form. But times and tastes are changing and here in America, since the mid-1970s, a media crossover has begun to take place. Since the advent of the "Star Wars phenomenon," the clear ideological division between science fiction and comics advocates has grown hazy. Devotees of pure prose are beginning to look at pictures, while panelology buffs are starting to appreciate words without illustrations. And here is where **ElfQuest** fits in.

ElfQuest is not a comic book. Neither is it a novel. It is a graphic novel, which means that words and pictures are intrinsic to each other's vitality. The story itself, however, is more complex and self-contained than most comic series published in this country. The strength of the overall plot has enabled **ElfQuest** to exist successfully as a prose novel, but words alone do not, in our own biased opinion, do the scope of the saga justice. Words and pictures—in this case neither stands perfectly without the other. The beauty of it is that **ElfQuest**'s audience is larger because of that realization. It has been said (and who are we to argue?) that **ElfQuest** is the first comic to cross the barrier and win the support of purists in the science fiction/fantasy field. But more than that, **ElfQuest** has helped pave the way for American comics to attain the same respected position as an art form which comics produced in Europe and Asia already enjoy. We are very proud of that.

Those involved in the production of this third color volume also have a right to be proud. Under Wendy's supervison, and along with Wendy herself, three excellent colorists, each with his or her own individual style, labored long summer hours with watercolor and brush against a breakneck deadline. That the results are so seamless is a testament to team effort. We defy anyone to guess who colored what—since there are pages which contain the work of all four colorists.

As to the story developments you find in this volume —we hope you will stay with us. Here we have entered a world of darkness and deception, a tomb of the living where vile secrets have been buried for ages and where the youth and innocence of the Wolfriders seem decidedly out of place. Old ideas are challenged, new dreams fly— and fall. And the most difficult moral dilemma that faces any leader is explored: which is wiser, to follow safe tradition or to pursue a vision of the future? Are ideals worth their possible consequences? The questions here are not easy; look for no easy answers in **ElfQuest Book 4.** The road the elves must now follow is a hard and uncertain one. The Quest goes on!

—Wendy and Richard Pini
Poughkeepsie, New York, 1983